Where to Launch on Inland Waterways

A guide to launching sites on
Britain's canals and rivers

Compiled by

Diana Hunter
and
Diana van der Klugt

Opus Book Publishing Limited

Acknowledgement
The Publishers would like to thank the many Local Authorities, Agencies and individuals who have helped to update this 2nd edition of the book

First edition 1993
Second edition 2001

ISBN 1-898574-09-X

20 The Strand, Steeple Ashton, Trowbridge, Wiltshire, BA14 6EP

Cover Design:
Dave Steele Mac Services

Printed by:
Biddles Ltd, Woodbridge Park Estate, Guildford

Contents

Introduction

Where to Launch on Inland Waterways is designed to serve as a guide to the location and availability of around 250 selected launching sites on the navigable rivers and canals of mainland Britain. It is intended to be useful to owners of all types of boats, from those launching small dinghies near home to those who regularly trail their boats in search of new cruising grounds, as well as the narrowboat owner wishing to move or launch a boat. This book is not a guide to the waterways themselves as there are already a number of excellent books and maps on the market which can be purchased from any good nautical bookshop or chandler.

The waterways included in this guide are listed alphabetically with a comprehensive index enabling the user to easily select sites. Each waterway is headed by a brief historic description followed by the name and address of the British Waterways area manager, Environment Agency or other body, which is in charge of the waterway.

Each site entry is headed by the name, address and phone number of the owner followed by concise site details. These include: size of craft that can be accommodated; the times when the site is available; restrictions as to its use, such as difficult or narrow access and locked gates; facilities available at or near the site i.e. fuel, water, parking [(c) indicates a charge], moorings and repairs; licensing authority (see next page); whether or not a charge is made and finally brief directions to the site and linking waterways.

Before visiting any site it is recommended that you contact the owner to ascertain its suitability for your particular needs and it should be appreciated that during busy summer weekends many boatyards and marinas are not able to accommodate casual launching.

This guide does not include an entry for every launching place on the inland waterways; sometimes it is impossible to obtain the information on a particular site or the owners or administrators of a site ask us not to include it in the book. However we have made every effort to research and include sites in most areas and on the majority of waterways.

While the information in this guide was correct at the time of going to press, changes in yard ownership are frequent and waterway restoration projects are progressing all the time. If you find something has changed or you know of a site that you feel should be included, please let us know. That way we can ensure that our next guide is as up-to-date and as helpful as possible.

Before Setting Out

Licences

In the majority of cases on the inland waterways, the boat owner is required to obtain a licence before launching a boat. The address and telephone number of the licensing authority for each waterway is given at the head of each section and should be contacted directly.

All British Waterway licences can be obtained from the following address:

Customer Services,
British Waterways,
Willow Grange, Church Road
Watford WD17 4QA

Telephone 01923 201120

Site charges

In most cases launching charges will be levied by the site owner, in addition to the licence fee already paid. Throughout the book we have used a sample charge for launching and retrieving a 15'/49m LOA craft. More specific details should be obtained where required using the contact number supplied.

Dimensions

This guide lists sites on both broad and narrow canals; before choosing your launching site be sure to ascertain the craft dimensions which a particular waterway can accommodate; these can be obtained from British Waterways or other licensing agency given in the introductory passage.

Insurance

Although it is not yet compulsory for all boats to be insured, most privately owned sites will require proof of third party insurance before launching is permitted. This is also required by licensing agencies before they will issue a licence.

Boat Safety Scheme

Owners of craft wishing to travel on the majority of the inland waterways will also require a current 'Boat Safety Certificate' showing that their boat meets the 'Boat Safety Scheme' standards in order to obtain a licence.

Restricted craft

In nearly all cases, the speed restrictions in force on inland waterways prohibit the use of speed boats and pwc (personal water craft). In a few cases however, there are derestricted zones where these activities may be permitted - further details will be found under the relevant entries.

Coastal sites

Launching sites on the coast of mainland Britain, on inland lakes and on the Norfolk Broads will be found in **Where to Launch Around the Coast** which is also published by Opus Book Publishing Limited.

AIRE AND CALDER CANAL — BW (North East Region)

Waterway Manager, British Waterways, Lock Lane, Castleford, West Yorks WF10 2LH — Tel: 01977 554351

Improvements to the River Aire were first made in 1700, enabling coal to be taken from the Yorkshire coalfields and agricultural produce to be brought in. The canal still carries a significant volume of commercial traffic. Speed limit on canal is 6 mph.

Goole Boathouse, Dutch Riverside, Goole, East Yorkshire

Tel: 01405 763985

Type:	concrete slipway (1:8)
Suits:	craft up to 36'/11m LOA and 11'6"/3.5m wide
Availability:	during working hours or at other times by prior arrangement
Restrictions:	none
Facilities:	diesel, parking for car and trailer, toilets, chandlery, gas, pump-out
Licence:	BW licence
Charge:	approx. £5
Directions:	leave M62 at junction 36: head towards Goole turning right at next three sets of traffic lights and follow signs to 'Waterway Museum'
Waters accessed:	Aire & Calder, Calder and Hebble and Leeds and Liverpool canals; Rivers Ouse and Trent and Humber Estuary

Stanley Ferry Marina, Ferry Lane, Stanley Ferry, Wakefield, West Yorks

Tel: 01924 201800

Type:	medium concrete slipway
Suits:	craft up to 22'/6.7m LOA
Availability:	0900 - 1730 Apr - Aug: 1000 - 1600 Sept - Mar by prior arrangement only
Restrictions:	locked barrier, speed limit 4 mph in marina
Facilities:	diesel, parking for car and trailer, boatbuilders, repairs, water, gas, pump-out, toilets and showers, chandlery, pub & restaurant: sewage and refuse disposal and overnight moorings nearby
Licence:	BW licence
Charge:	approx. £10
Directions:	leave M62 at junction 30 and take the A642 south towards Wakefield following signs to Stanley Ferry Marina
Waters accessed:	Aire & Calder, Calder and Hebble and Leeds and Liverpool canals; Rivers Ouse and Trent and Humber Estuary

RIVER ANCHOLME — EA (Anglian Region)

Kingfisher House, Goldhay Way, Orton Goldhay, Peterborough PE2 OZR
Tel: 01733 371811

The river is navigable for approximately 25 miles from the entrance from the River Humber at South Ferriby to Bishopsbridge. There is a speed limit of 7 mph from South Ferriby to Brigg, and 4 mph on the rest of the river. Before entering the river, inform the lock-keeper at South Ferriby Tel: 01652 635219: the lock is manned 24 hours a day from 1st April - 30th October. From 1 November - 31 March lock-keepers available by prior arrangement only during normal working hours.

Clapson Marina, Red Lane, South Ferriby, Barton on Humber, Humberside
Tel: 01652 635620

Type:	launching by crane only
Suits:	larger craft
Availability:	during working hours by prior arrangement only
Restrictions:	launching by crane only - no slipway
Facilities:	diesel, petrol nearby, parking for car and trailer(c), toilets, chandlery, repairs
Licence:	EA licence
Charge:	yes - on application
Directions:	turn off A1077 Scunthorpe to Barton Road at South Ferriby Sluice
Waters accessed:	River Ancholme, tidal River Humber and North Sea via South Ferriby lock

RIVER ARUN

Littlehampton Harbour Board, Harbour Office, Pier Road, Littlehampton, West Sussex
Tel: 01903 721215

Navigable for approx. 24 miles inland; tides run strongly in the lower reaches of the river which is tidal to Pallingham. There is a speed limit of 6½ knots from Littlehampton to Arundel Bridge and 5½ knots above Arundel Bridge.

Littlehampton Marina, Ferry Road, Littlehampton, West Sussex
Tel: 01903 713553

Type:	wide shallow concrete slipway
Suits:	powered craft except pwc
Availability:	approx. 4 hours either side HW 0800 - 1700 by prior arrangement
Restrictions:	launching by yard staff only and insurance certificate required for craft; tides run very strongly in river entrance; water-skiing, windsurfing and pwc prohibited
Facilities:	fuel, parking for car and trailer, toilets and showers, chandlery, dive shop, crane and hoist (for craft up to 45 tons), outboard repairs and full boatyard facilities; site for tents and camper vans
Licence:	harbour dues approx. £5
Charge:	approx. £20 mon - fri, £25 sat, sun & BH

Directions:	from Chichester follow A27 east to Arundel taking the A284 then A259; cross the river and turn left after ½ mile: site is on west bank downstream of bridge
Waters accessed:	River Arun and open sea (1 mile downstream)

Fisherman's Quay, Surrey Street, Littlehampton, West Sussex

Tel: 01903 721215 (Harbour Office)

Type:	steep concrete slipway (1:7), with sharp lip at summit, onto mud
Suits:	all craft except pwc
Availability:	all states of tide but concrete only to half tide mark, thereafter compacted mud: beware strong currents in river entrance especially at springs
Restrictions:	may require 4-wheel drive vehicle; water-skiing, windsurfing and pwc prohibited
Facilities:	fuel from local garage, parking for car and trailer under 14'/4.3m long on site (c), chandlery, diving supplies and outboard repairs adjacent
Licence:	harbour dues approx. £5
Charge:	small fee may be payable
Directions:	from Arundel follow A284 and signs to town centre: site is at end of Surrey St on east bank of river adjacent to lifeboat station
Waters accessed:	River Arun and open sea

Ship and Anchor Marina, Ford, Nr. Arundel, West Sussex

Tel: 01243 551262

Type:	concrete slipway
Suits:	powered craft up to24'/7.3m LOA
Availability:	for approx. 4 hours either side HW 0900 - 1730
Restrictions:	launching by yard staff only using tractor at owner's risk: insurance certificate required for craft; pwc prohibited
Facilities:	parking for car and trailer, toilets, campsite and pub
Licence:	none
Charge:	approx. £25
Directions:	from A27 at Arundel take the Ford road: site is on left after the station
Waters accessed:	River Arun and open sea

Old Swan Bridge, Swan Corner, Pulborough, West Sussex

Type:	steep concrete slipway with turning space and snatch blocks at top
Suits:	canoes and small powered craft up to 15'/4.6m LOA
Availability:	near HW only
Restrictions:	access is narrow and difficult: a minimum 40m of rope is required to lower boat; pwc prohibited
Facilities:	fuel nearby, limited parking at station nearby (c), toilets nearby, pub and shops
Licence:	none
Charge:	none

Directions:	turn off the A29 Bognor road at junction with A283: site is adjacent east side of bridge on north bank
Waters accessed:	River Arun and open sea

ASHBY CANAL **(BW Midlands Region)**

Waterway Manager, British Waterways, Fradley Junction, Fradley, Alrewas, Burton-upon-Trent, Staffordshire DE13 7DN Tel: 01283 790236

Originally planned to connect the Coventry Canal to the River Trent, the canal was actually only built as far as Moira, but prospered transporting high quality coal from the Ashby Coalfields to southern England. Some of the canal has now been abandoned but it is navigable for nearly 22 miles to Snarestone: there are no locks. Speed limit is 4 mph.

Snarestone, Leics

Tel: 01455 290129 (Ashby Canal Association)

Type:	steep steel slipway
Suits:	small powered craft, canoes and rowing dinghies
Availability:	by key which can be hired by members - £10 pa
Restrictions:	locked gate, for use of members only
Facilities:	parking for car & trailer and toilets on site: rubbish, sewage disposal and water nearby, BW key required
Licence:	BW licence
Charge:	yes - for hire of key
Directions:	turn off A5 north of Nuneaton onto A444 to Twycross, then turn right onto B4116 to Snarestone: turn left into Quarry Lane; site is after ¼ mile on left
Waters accessed:	Ashby and Coventry canals and main inland waterway system

RIVER AVON (Bristol) **BW (South West Region)**

Waterway Manager, British Waterways, Llanthony Warehouse, Gloucester Docks, Gloucester GL1 2EH Tel: 01452 525524

The canalised river is tidal as far as Hanham Lock and is controlled by the Port of Bristol Authority. Between Hanham and Bath it is controlled by BW with whom any boat using this stretch of the river should be registered. There is no public right of navigation above Pulteney Weir in Bath and there is a speed limit of 4 mph on the river. The Kennet and Avon Canal joins the river in Bath, immediately after Bath Bottom (deep) lock.

Saltford Marina, The Shallows, Saltford, Nr. Bristol, Avon

Tel: 01225 872226 Fax: 01225 874886

Type:	concrete slipway
Suits:	craft up to 27'/8.2m LOA with draught less than 3'/0.9m
Availability:	during daylight hours
Restrictions:	none
Facilities:	diesel, petrol nearby, parking for car and trailer, refuse disposal, water, toilets and showers, overnight moorings, chandlery, boatyard, crane by arrangement, bar and restaurant

Licence: BW licence
Charge: yes - on application
Directions: access is from the A4 Bristol to Bath road turning into The Shallows (Bath end). It is best to head into The Shallows from Bath due to a very tight left hand turn encountered if coming from Bristol
Waters accessed: Kennet and Avon Canal, Bristol Channel and Rivers Avon & Severn

Bristol Boat Centre, Mead Lane, Saltford, Nr Bristol, Avon

Tel: 01225 872032

Type: concrete slipway onto shingle
Suits: sailing craft, canoes and rowing dinghies up to 20'/6.1m LOA
Availability: daily 1000 - 1730 in summer by prior arrangement: closed sun
Restrictions: narrow access road with locked barrier, restricted height
Facilities: fuel nearby; parking for car and trailer, toilets, gas, water, chandlery, outboard repairs all on site
Licence: BW licence
Charge: approx. £5
Directions: follow the A4 Bath to Bristol road turning off to Saltford Lock; site is adjacent 'Jolly Sailor'
Waters accessed: Kennet and Avon Canal, Bristol Channel and Rivers Avon & Severn

Lock and Weir Pub, Hanham, Bristol, Avon

Tel: 0117 967 3793

Type: concrete slipway
Suits: craft up to 23'/7m LOA
Availability: by arrangement during daylight hours
Restrictions: steep slipway: check for availability
Facilities: fuel, parking for car and trailer, refuse disposal, water, toilets, overnight moorings, pub
Licence: BW licence
Charge: yes - on application
Directions: turn off A431 at Hanham and follow minor roads to lock
Waters accessed: Kennet and Avon Canal, Bristol Channel and Rivers Avon & Severn

RIVER AVON (Warwickshire)

Evesham Lock to Alveston Sluice - Upper Avon Navigation Trust, Bridge 63, Harvington, Evesham, Worcs WR11 5NR Tel: 01386 870526

Evesham Lock to Tewkesbury - Lower Avon Navigation Trust, Mill Wharf, Mill Lane, Wyre Piddle, Pershore, Worcs WR10 2JF Tel: 01386 552517

The river is navigable for just over 45 miles from Alveston Sluice, north of Stratford-on-Avon, to its junction with the River Severn a short distance below Mythe Bridge in Tewkesbury. There is a speed limit of 6 mph on the Lower Avon and 4 mph on the Upper Avon. There are proposals to extend the navigation north to Leamington Spa to link with the Grand Union Canal main line.

Bancroft Cruisers, Clopton Bridge, Stratford-on-Avon, Warks
Tel: 01789 269669

Type:	concrete slipway
Suits:	small powered craft
Availability:	approx. 0930 - 1730 daily
Restrictions:	check for availability
Facilities:	gas
Licence:	Upper Avon
Charge:	yes - on application
Directions:	access is from the A3400 gyratory one-way system in the town centre via signposted driveway adjacent to the Moat House International Hotel by Clopton Bridge
Waters accessed:	Stratford-on-Avon Canal, Rivers Avon & Severn and Bristol Channel

Welford Boat Station, Synder Meadow Lane, Welford-on-Avon, Warks
Tel: 01789 750878

Type:	concrete slipway with medium gradient
Suits:	small powered craft, canoes and rowing dinghies
Availability:	by prior arrangement only: assistance available
Restrictions:	narrow road; locked barrier
Facilities:	diesel, parking for car and trailer, chandlery, sewage disposal, water, overnight moorings on site; petrol and pubs nearby
Licence:	Upper Avon
Charge:	approx. £5
Directions:	from Stratford on Avon follow B439 towards Bidford-on-Avon turning right to Welford; Synder Meadow Lane is 200m on right
Waters accessed:	Stratford-on-Avon Canal, Rivers Avon & Severn and Bristol Channel

Bidford Boats, 4 The Pleck, Bidford-on-Avon, Warks
Tel: 01789 773205

Type:	concrete slipway
Suits:	craft up to 25'/7.6m LOA
Availability:	0900 - 1800 daily in summer by prior arrangement

Restrictions:	none, but please telephone in advance
Facilities:	diesel, petrol from garage nearby, parking for car and trailer(c), sewage disposal, water, pump-out, boat hire, skippered charter, overnight moorings
Licence:	Upper Avon available Evesham Lock
Charge:	yes - on application
Directions:	follow A439 west from Stratford-upon-Avon to Bidford-on-Avon: entrance is opposite the Reliance Garage
Waters accessed:	Stratford-on-Avon Canal, Rivers Avon & Severn and Bristol Channel

Evesham Marina, King's Road, Evesham, Worcs

Tel: 01386 47813

Type:	medium concrete slipway
Suits:	all shallow-draught craft
Availability:	0900 - 1700 daily
Restrictions:	none
Facilities:	fuel, parking for car and trailer(c), refuse disposal, water, gas, pump-out, toilets, overnight moorings, boatyard, engine repairs
Licence:	Upper Avon
Charge:	approx.£5
Directions:	leave M5 at junction 7 following A44 east to Evesham
Waters accessed:	Stratford-on-Avon Canal, Rivers Avon & Severn and Bristol Channel

Sankey Marine, Worcester Road, Evesham, Worcs

Tel: 01386 442338 Fax: 01386 49011

Type:	concrete slipway
Suits:	small powered craft
Availability:	0800 - 1800 daily in summer
Restrictions:	none
Facilities:	fuel, parking for car and trailer(c), water, gas, toilets and showers, overnight moorings, chandlery and yard facilities, engine repairs
Licence:	Lower Avon
Charge:	yes - on application
Directions:	leave M5 at junction 7 following the A44 east to Pershore, turning onto the B4083/B4084: site is below the Abbey Manor House
Waters accessed:	Stratford-on-Avon Canal, Rivers Avon & Severn and Bristol Channel

Sanders Boatyard, Pensham Road, Pershore, Worcs

Tel: 01386 552765

Type:	steep slipway
Suits:	all craft up to 30'/9.1m LOA
Availability:	0900 - 1300 and 1400 - 1800 daily
Restrictions:	none

Facilities: fuel, parking for car and trailer(c), toilets, chandlery and boatyard
Licence: Lower Avon
Charge: yes - on application
Directions: turn off M5, at junction 7 onto A44: at Pershore new bridge turn right then fork right and the entrance drive is on the right
Waters accessed: Stratford-on-Avon Canal, Rivers Avon & Severn and Bristol Channel

Bredon Marina, Dock Lane, Bredon, Glos

Tel: 01684 773166

Type: shallow concrete slipway
Suits: all craft up to 20'/6.1m LOA
Availability: by prior arrangement
Restrictions: ribs, windsurfers and pwc prohibited
Facilities: diesel, parking for car and trailer, toilets, water, gas, moorings, chandlery and boatyard, engine repairs, crane
Licence: Lower Avon available at marina
Charge: approx. £5
Directions: from Tewkesbury take B4080 and after 3 miles turn left towards church; marina is ½ mile down road on left
Waters accessed: Stratford-on-Avon Canal, Rivers Avon & Severn and Bristol Channel

Tewkesbury Marina, Bredon Road, Tewkesbury, Glos

Tel: 01684 293737 Fax: 01684 293076

Type: hoist only
Suits: larger craft
Availability: during weekday working hours by arrangement only
Restrictions: no slipway: launching by hoist only
Facilities: fuel, trailers can be left(c), toilets and showers, sewage and refuse disposal, water, gas, pump-out, overnight moorings, chandlery and boatyard, engine repairs
Licence: Lower Avon
Charge: approx. £70
Directions: leave M5 at junction 9, taking A438 then A38 and B4080: site is near confluence with River Severn
Waters accessed: Stratford-on-Avon Canal, Rivers Avon & Severn and Bristol Channel

Basingstoke Canal Authority, The Canal Centre, Mytchett Place Road, Mytchett, Surrey GU16 6DD Tel: 01252 370073

The canal is now navigable from Woodham Junction, where it joins the River Wey, for nearly 31 miles to the limit of navigation just before Greywell Tunnel. Before launching, a licence should be obtained from the canal office. There is a speed limit of 4 mph on the canal.

Potters Pub Slipway, Mytchett Place Road, Mytchett, Surrey

Type: concrete slipway
Suits: small craft: approx. depth of water 2'6"/0.8m
Availability: during daylight hours: purchase key from BCA office
Restrictions: locked barrier
Facilities: parking for car and trailer at canal centre opposite: pub adjacent
Licence: BCA (see above)
Charge: included in licence fee
Directions: follow A321 north from Farnborough and signs to Mytchett: site is north of Mytchett Lake on the east side of the canal
Waters accessed: Basingstoke Canal, River Wey and River Thames

Farnborough Road Wharf, Aldershot, Surrey

Type: concrete slipway
Suits: small craft: approx. depth of water 2'6"/0.8m
Availability: during daylight hours: purchase key from BCA office
Restrictions: inaccessible during biennial Army/Air Show, locked barrier
Facilities: parking for car and trailer
Licence: BCA (see above)
Charge: included in licence fee
Directions: turn off A325 dual carriageway south of canal onto A323 towards Fleet: access to site is via one-way system just after passing under the dual carriageway
Waters accessed: Basingstoke Canal, River Wey and River Thames

Barley Mow Slipway, Winchfield, Hants

Type: concrete slipway
Suits: small craft: approx. depth of water 2'6"/0.8m
Availability: during daylight hours: purchase key from BCA office
Restrictions: awkward slipway on rising ground; locked barrier
Facilities: parking for car and trailer, Barley Mow Pub nearby
Licence: BCA (see above)
Charge: included in licence fee
Directions: from Aldershot follow A323 west to Fleet turning off to follow signs: site is on east side of Barley Mow bridge
Waters accessed: Basingstoke Canal, River Wey and River Thames

Galleon Marine, Colt Hill, Odiham, Hants

Tel: 01256 703691

Type:	steep concrete slipway
Suits:	craft up to 25'/7.6m LOA max with suitable towing vehicle
Availability:	0900 - 1700 daily in summer: closed sun in winter
Restrictions:	none
Facilities:	diesel, parking for car and trailer (c), sewage and refuse disposal, water, gas, pump-out, chandlery on site; petrol and toilets nearby
Licence:	BCA (see above)
Charge:	approx. £10
Directions:	leave M3 at junction 5, taking the A287 east and turning right at either end of the bypass into Odiham Village
Waters accessed:	Basingstoke Canal, River Wey and River Thames

BIRMINGHAM CANAL NAVIGATIONS BW (Midlands Region)

Waterway Manager, British Waterways, Bayleys Lane, Tipton,
West Midlands DY4 0PX Tel: 121 506 1300

The first canal was built from Aldersley on the Staffordshire and Worcestershire Canal to Birmingham and the complex network which subsequently developed was the result of three rival companies each trying to monopolise the traffic. Over 100 miles of the network are still navigable. Speed limit is 4 mph.

Norton Canes Boatbuilders, Norton Canes Dock, Lime Lane, Pelsall, West Midlands

Tel: 01543 374888

Type:	crane only
Suits:	larger craft
Availability:	during working hours by prior arrangement only
Restrictions:	no slipway: launching by crane only
Facilities:	fuel, parking for car and trailer, sewage and refuse disposal, water, overnight moorings, boatyard
Licence:	BW
Charge:	yes - on application
Directions:	leave M6 at junction 12 following A5 east: site is between Cannock and Brownhills
Waters accessed:	Worcs and Birmingham, Birmingham and Fazeley, Staffs and Worcs, Shropshire Union and Grand Union canals

Hockley Port Ltd, Canal Moorings, All Saints Street, Hockley, Birmingham

Tel: 0121-507 0477

Type:	shallow concrete slipway into canal basin
Suits:	small powered craft, canoes and rowing dinghies
Availability:	0800 to 2000 by prior arrangement
Restrictions:	none
Facilities:	parking for car and trailer, water, toilets, dry dock

Licence: BW licence
Charge: approx. £5
Directions: telephone for directions: site is on Birmingham Level off Soho Loop
Waters accessed: Birmingham Canal Navigations, Worcs and Birmingham, Birmingham and Fazeley, Staffs and Worcs, Shropshire Union and Grand Union canals

Coombeswood Canal Trust, Hawne Basin, Hereward Rise, Halesowen
Tel: 01384 373298

Type: shallow concrete slipway with cradle
Suits: small powered craft or larger craft using cradle
Availability: by prior arrangement only
Restrictions: phone for availability: steel rails on slip may obstruct trailers; speed limit dead slow in basin
Facilities: diesel on site, petrol nearby, parking for car and trailer, sewage and refuse disposal, water, gas, pump-out, toilets and showers, chandlery, boatyard, laundry room, DIY facilities
Licence: BW licence
Charge: approx. £20
Directions: from Halesowen, take the Dudley road (A459) turning right into Hereward Rise: site is at top of hill on right: ring bell
Waters accessed: Birmingham Canal Navigations, Worcs and Birmingham, Birmingham and Fazeley, Staffs and Worcs, Shropshire Union and Grand Union canals

Brecon and Abergavenny Canal - see page 46

BRIDGEWATER CANAL Manchester Ship Canal Company

Property Division, 7th Floor, Quay West, Trafford Wharf Road, Manchester M17 1PL Tel: 0161 872 2411

Built to transport coal from the Duke of Bridgewater's mines at Worsley to Manchester, the canal was later extended to join the Trent and Mersey Canal at Preston Brook and the Leeds and Liverpool Canal at Leigh. The canal carried commercial traffic until 1974. Speed limit on canal is 4 mph.

Hesford Marine, Warrington Lane, Lymm, Cheshire
Tel: 01925 754639

Type: concrete slipway
Suits: all craft less than 7'/2.1m wide
Availability: during working hours by prior arrangement
Restrictions: check for availability
Facilities: diesel, water, gas, toilets, overnight moorings (occasionally), chandlery and boatyard, crane by arrangement
Licence: BW but additional charge for using Pomona Lock into Manchester Ship Canal. Further information from

	Manchester Ship Canal Co, address and tel. as above
Charge:	approx. £30
Directions:	leave M6 at junction 20 taking A50 to High Legh: turn left onto B5212 and turn right at bottom of hill into Warrington Lane
Waters accessed:	Bridgewater, Trent and Mersey, Rochdale and Leeds and Liverpool canals

Lymm Marina, Warrington Lane, Lymm, Cheshire

Tel: 01925 752945

Type:	concrete slipway
Suits:	shallow draught craft only
Availability:	during working hours by prior arrangement only
Restrictions:	none
Facilities:	diesel, parking for car and trailer(c), refuse disposal, water, gas, toilets, chandlery and boatyard
Licence:	BW but additional charge for using Pomona Lock into Manchester Ship Canal. Further information from Manchester Ship Canal Co, address and tel. as above
Charge:	approx. £10
Directions:	leave M6 at junction 20 taking A50 to High Legh: turn left onto B5212 and turn right at bottom of hill into Warrington Lane
Waters accessed:	Bridgewater, Trent and Mersey, Rochdale and Leeds and Liverpool canals

Preston Brook Marina, Marina Lane, Runcorn, Cheshire

Tel:01928 716666

Type:	shallow concrete slipway
Suits:	small powered craft, canoes and rowing dinghies
Availability:	during working hours by prior arrangement
Restrictions:	access by narrow road; security gates
Facilities:	fuel nearby, parking for car and trailer (c), sewage and refuse disposal, water, gas, toilets, shower, shops in walking distance
Licence:	BW but additional charge for using Pomona Lock into Manchester Ship Canal. Further information from Manchester Ship Canal Co, address and tel. as above
Charge:	approx. £10
Directions:	turn off M56 at junction 11 taking A56 to Preston Brook: at third roundabout follow signs to Marina down Murdishaw Avenue; site is on Runcorn Branch of canal below bridge 67
Waters accessed:	Bridgewater, Trent and Mersey, Rochdale and Leeds and Liverpool canals

BRIDGWATER AND TAUNTON CANAL

BW (South West Region)

Wateway Manager, British Waterways, The Wharf, Govilon, Abergavenny, Gwent NP7 9NY Tel: 01873 830328 Fax: 01873 831788

This attractive canal runs for 15 miles from Bridgwater to Taunton in Somerset. Originally conceived as part of a scheme to join the Bristol and English Channels it was mainly used to transport coal & iron to Taunton and agricultural produce to Bridgwater docks. Speed limit on canal is 4 mph.

Bridgwater YMCA, Friarn Avenue, Bridgwater, Somerset
Tel:01278 422511

Type:	shallow concrete slipway
Suits:	small powered craft, canoes and rowing dinghies
Availability:	by prior arrangement
Restrictions:	none
Facilities:	fuel nearby, parking for car and trailer, toilets, community building and grounds on site, chandlery nearby, engine repairs nearby
Licence:	BW licence
Charge:	approx.£3
Directions:	from M5 junction 24 follow A38 to Bridgwater; at round-about turn left into North Broadway then left into Albert Street; Friarn Avenue is on the left.
Waters accessed:	Bridgwater and Taunton Canal, River Tone

Bathpool Moorings, Swingbridge, Bathpool, Taunton, Somerset

Type:	short steep concrete slipway
Suits:	small powered craft, canoes and rowing dinghies
Availability:	at all times for BW keyholders
Restrictions:	access down narrow track with gate opened by BW key
Facilities:	fuel nearby, parking for car and trailer, water
Licence:	BW licence
Charge:	none
Directions:	from Taunton follow A38 towards Bridgwater through Bathpool; turn left after canal bridge and follow signs to canal car park
Waters accessed:	Bridgwater and Taunton Canal, River Tone

CALDER AND HEBBLE NAVIGATION **BW (North East Region)**

Wateway Manager, British Waterways, Lock Lane, Castleford,
West Yorks WF10 2LH Tel: 01977 554351

Constructed to improve the River Calder above Wakefield, this navigation was never as successful as the Aire and Calder which it joins at Fall Ing Lock in Wakefield, running for just over 18 miles to Sowerby Bridge. Speed limit on canal is 4 mph.

Shire Cruisers, The Wharf, Sowerby Bridge, West Yorks

Tel: 01422 832712 Fax: 01422 839565 e-mail: nigel@shirecruisers.co.uk

Type:	shallow concrete slipway
Suits:	powered craft up to 23'/7m LOA, canoes & rowing dinghies
Availability:	0900 - 1700 mon to fri: 1000 - 1600 sat; sun 1200 - 1400 in summer
Restrictions:	no speedboats
Facilities:	diesel, parking for car and trailer(c), sewage and refuse disposal, water, toilets, moorings, chandlery and boatyard, engine repairs, hirefleet all on site; station, shops & petrol nearby
Licence:	BW licence available on site
Charge:	approx. £30
Directions:	follow A58 west from Halifax to east end of Sowerby Bridge; turn in by sculpture of lock-keeper and boy
Waters accessed:	Calder & Hebble and Aire and Calder Navigations, Huddersfield Broad & Narrow canals and Rochdale Canal

Elland Wharf, Elland, West Yorks

Tel: 0161 427 7723 (Lockside Estates)

Type:	concrete slipway
Suits:	all craft: into approx. 5'/1.5m water
Availability:	0800 - 2000 daily
Restrictions:	get permission to launch and key from Lockside Estates or Mr. W Carey (Junior), Wharf House
Facilities:	parking for car and trailer
Licence:	BW licence
Charge:	yes - on application
Directions:	from Bradford, follow A641 south and A6025 through Elland, turning off into Gas Works Lane (off Elland Bridge) and onto Elland Wharf
Waters accessed:	Calder & Hebble and Aire and Calder Navigations, Huddersfield Broad & Narrow canals and Rochdale Canal

Robinsons Hire Cruisers, Dewsbury, West Yorks

Tel: 01924 467976

Type:	concrete slipway
Suits:	craft up to 57'/17.3m LOA and 3'/0.9m draught
Availability:	during working hours by prior arrangement
Restrictions:	none
Facilities:	fuel, parking for car and trailer(c), refuse and sewage

	disposal, water, gas, pump-out, toilets and showers, overnight moorings, boatyard with crane/winch by arrangement
Licence:	BW licence
Charge:	yes - on application
Directions:	from Leeds follow A62 south, turning into Mill Street East in Dewsbury: site is on the Dewsbury Arm
Waters accessed:	Calder & Hebble and Aire and Calder Navigations, Huddersfield Broad & Narrow canals and Rochdale Canal

CALEDONIAN CANAL — BW (Scotland Region)

Waterway Manager, Canal Office, Seaport Marina, Muirtown Basin, Muirtown, Inverness IV3 5LS Tel: 01463 233140

The canal runs across Scotland for 60 miles from Fort William on the west coast to Inverness on the east coast, giving access to Loch Lochy, Loch Oich and Loch Ness. There is a speed limit of 6 mph on the canal sections.

Caley Marina, Canal Road, Inverness

Tel: 01463 236539

Type:	fairly steep slipway into 6'/1.8m water
Suits:	craft up to 21'/6.4m LOA
Availability:	0900 - 1730 mon to sat by prior arrangement
Restrictions:	pwc prohibited
Facilities:	diesel, petrol nearby, parking for car and trailer (c), toilets, overnight moorings, chandlery, engine repairs and boatyard with crane by arrangement
Licence:	obtain BW licence from office
Charge:	approx. £5
Directions:	leave A9 following signs for the A862 across Inverness to Muirtown swing bridge: turn up canal road by the flight of locks
Waters accessed:	Caledonian Canal and Loch Ness

Tomnahurich Bridge, Inverness

Tel: 01463 233140 (Canal Office)

Type:	steep slipway into approx. 5'/1.5m water
Suits:	small craft only
Availability:	during working hours 0800 - 1730 daily
Restrictions:	contact Canal Office prior to arrival to discuss requirements
Facilities:	fuel nearby, parking for car and trailer by arrangement, toilets, chandlery and outboard repairs nearby
Licence:	obtain BW licence from Canal Office
Charge:	none
Directions:	follow A9 to Inverness, then turn onto A82 and turn right at Tomnahurich Bridge
Waters accessed:	Caledonian Canal and Loch Ness

Monster Activities, Great Glen Water Park, South Laggan, By Spean Bridge, Invernesshire

Tel: 01809 501340

Type:	steep slipway into approx. 4'/1.2m water
Suits:	all craft up to 20'/6.1m LOA
Availability:	0900 - 2100 daily by prior arrangement
Restrictions:	6 mph speed limit on canal & near moored craft
Facilities:	fuel nearby, parking for car and trailer(c), water, toilets, overnight moorings, watersports centre, laundry, swimming pool, sauna, restaurant and bar
Licence:	none for Loch Oich but BW licence for canal
Charge:	approx. £10
Directions:	follow A82 from Fort William 22 miles towards Inverness turning right just before South Laggan swing bridge: site is at south west end of Loch Oich
Waters accessed:	Loch Oich and Caledonian Canal

CHELMER AND BLACKWATER NAVIGATION

Chelmer and Blackwater Navigation Ltd

Paper Mill Lock, Little Baddow,Chelmsford, Essex CM3 4BF

Tel: 01245 222025

Until 1974 this was a working canal and is still owned by the company which founded it in 1793. The canal links Chelmsford to the sea at Maldon, a distance of 14 miles. There is a speed limit of 4 mph.

Paper Mill Lock, Little Baddow, Chelmsford, Essex

Tel: 01245 222025

Type:	shallow concrete slipway
Suits:	craft up to 60'/18.3m LOA, 12'/3.6m beam and 3'/0.9m draught
Availability:	by prior arrangement only
Restrictions:	none
Facilities:	fuel (3 miles), parking for car and trailer by arrangement, toilets and outboard repairs
Licence:	from Chelmer and Blackwater Navigation Ltd
Charge:	approx. £24
Directions:	from A12, take A414 to Maldon, turning left at Danbury duck pond to Little Baddow; go down the hill for 2½ miles and lock house yard is just before the river bridge
Waters accessed:	Chelmer & Blackwater Canal, Blackwater Estuary and North Sea

Waterway Manager, British Waterways, The Kiln, Mather Lane, Newark, Nottighamshire NG24 4TT Tel: 01636 704481

The canal was originally built to facilitate the transport of goods from the Chesterfield area to the sea via the River Trent and ran from Chesterfield to West Stockwith where it joined the river. The navigable section now runs from Worksop to West Stockwith, a distance of 25½ miles: the river lock is manned Tel: (01427) 890204 and is normally accessible from 2½ hours before to 4½ hours after HW. There is a speed limit of 4 mph on the canal.

West Stockwith Basin, West Stockwith, Nr. Doncaster, South Yorkshire
Tel: 01427 890204

Type:	shallow concrete slipway
Suits:	craft up to 55'/16.7m LOA
Availability:	1½ hours before HW to 5½ hours after during daylight hours by prior arrangement with lock-keeper
Restrictions:	BW key required for access; Weighton Road Bridge restricted to 3 tons but alternative access available
Facilities:	diesel, parking for car and trailer, gas, toilets, chandlery, outboard repairs all on site
Licence:	BW licence
Charge:	approx. £10
Directions:	turn off A631 west of Gainsborough onto A161 Goole road turning right to West Stockwith after passing through Misterton
Waters accessed:	Chesterfield Canal, River Trent, Humber Estuary and the North Sea

Shireoaks Marina, Shireoaks, Worksop, Notts
Tel: 01909 489145

Type:	shallow concrete slipway
Suits:	small powered craft
Availability:	by prior arrangement only
Restrictions:	height restriction on one of the access roads
Facilities:	parking for car and trailer, toilets
Licence:	BW licence
Charge:	none at present
Directions:	follow A57 from Worksop
Waters accessed:	Chesterfield canal

Waterway Manager, British Waterways, Fradley Junction, Fradley, Alrewas, Burton-upon-Trent, Staffordshire DE13 7DN Tel: 01283 790236

This canal runs for 38 miles from Coventry Basin to Fradley Junction and was built to connect Coventry with the Trent and Mersey Canal and to provide cheap coal from Bedworth coalfield. This was one of the most prosperous canals having links with the Trent and Mersey, the Birmingham and Fazeley at Fazeley Junction, the Ashby at Marston Junction and the Oxford at Hawkesbury Junction. Speed limit is 4 mph.

Swan Lane Wharf, Swan Lane, Stoke Heath, Coventry, West Midlands
Tel: 024 7625 8864

Type:	concrete slipway
Suits:	craft up to 20'/6.1m LOA
Availability:	0900 - 1700 mon - fri by prior arrangement
Restrictions:	fairly steep slipway into 2'/0.6m water
Facilities:	fuel, parking for car and trailer(c), sewage and refuse disposal, water, pump-out, toilets, overnight moorings, chandlery and boatyard, engine repairs
Licence:	BW licence
Charge:	yes - on application
Directions:	leave M6 at junction 2 taking A4600 towards City centre: after passing under railway bridge turn first right into Swan Lane
Waters accessed:	Trent and Mersey, Birmingham and Fazeley, Ashby and Oxford canals

Alvecote Marina, Robeys Lane, Alvecote, Tamworth, Staffordshire
Tel: 01827 898585

Type:	shallow concrete slipway
Suits:	small powered craft
Availability:	by prior arrangement only
Restrictions:	none
Facilities:	diesel, parking for car and trailer (c), toilets, electricity, water, moorings all on site; petrol nearby
Licence:	BW licence
Charge:	approx. £10
Directions:	from junction10 on M42 follow A5 towards Tamworth turning north onto B5080; at junction with B5000 turn right towards Polesworth then first left to Alvecote
Waters accessed:	Coventry, Trent and Mersey, Birmingham and Fazeley, Ashby and Oxford canals

RIVER DEE **Council of the City of Chester**

Town Hall, Chester CH1 2HN Tel: 01244 325681

The river is navigable from Chester to Farndon. There is a speed limit of 6 mph.

Dee Fords, Sandy Lane, Chester, Cheshire

Tel: 01244 325681

Type:	shallow concrete slipway
Suits:	small powered craft
Availability:	during daylight hours
Restrictions:	none
Facilities:	fuel nearby, parking for car and trailer(c), toilets, chandlery nearby
Licence:	from the Director of Environmental Health
Charge:	approx. £10
Directions:	follow B5130 1½ miles south from Chester
Waters accessed:	River Dee

FORTH AND CLYDE CANAL **BW (Scotland Region)**

Waterway Manager, Lowland Canal Office, Rosebank House, Camelon, Falkirk FK1 4DS Tel: 01324 671217

Originally built to link the Firth of Clyde on the West Coast and the Firth of Forth on the East Coast, the canal runs from Bowling in the west to Grangemouth in the east and is 56km/35 miles long. A link with the Union Canal (see page 98) will be achieved once the Falkirk Wheel opens in Spring 2002. There is a speed limit of 6 mph and a height restriction of 9'10"/3m on the canal. The canal depth is approx. 6'/1.8m. Further information from Canal Office or www.scottishcanals.co.uk.

Hay's Slip, Southbank Road, Kirkintilloch, Strathclyde

Type:	concrete slipway
Suits:	all craft: large slip with good surface
Availability:	during daylight hours
Restrictions:	none
Facilities:	petrol nearby, parking for car and trailer on site
Licence:	BW licence from Canal Office
Charge:	none
Directions:	follow the A803 from Glasgow to Kirkintilloch turning off into Southbank Road
Waters accessed:	Forth & Clyde and Union canals (link opening early 2002)

Stables Inn, Glasgow Road Bridge, Kirkintilloch, Strathclyde

Tel: 01836-704 287 (Canalside Leisure Ltd),

Type:	concrete slipway
Suits:	all craft: large slipway with rails and boat trolley and small ramp
Availability:	during daylight hours
Restrictions:	none
Facilities:	fuel nearby, parking for car and trailer

Licence:	BW licence from Canal Office
Charge:	yes - on application
Directions:	follow A803 1½ miles west of Kirkintilloch
Waters accessed:	Forth & Clyde and Union canals (link opening early 2002)

Sandbank Street, Maryhill, Strathclyde

Type:	stone on timber ramp
Suits:	craft up to 13'/4m LOA
Availability:	during daylight hours
Restrictions:	access ramp is quite steep
Facilities:	no fuel
Licence:	BW licence from Canal Office
Charge:	none
Directions:	follow A81 north west from Glasgow
Waters accessed:	Forth & Clyde and Union canals (link opening early 2002)

Firhill Basin

Type:	stone ramp
Suits:	craft up to 13'/4m LOA
Availability:	during daylight hours
Restrictions:	none
Facilities:	no fuel, parking for car and trailer
Licence:	BW licence from Canal Office
Charge:	none
Directions:	access is via Firhill Road, site is adjacent road bridge
Waters accessed:	Forth & Clyde and Union canals (link opening early 2002)

Auchinstarry, nr Kilsyth, Strathclyde

Type:	concrete slipway
Suits:	craft up to 25'/7.6m LOA
Availability:	during daylight hours
Restrictions:	none
Facilities:	no fuel, parking for car and trailer
Licence:	BW licence from Canal Office
Charge:	none
Directions:	follow A803 towards Kilsyth, turning onto B802: site is located next to BW depot and access road is immediately adjacent to bridge
Waters accessed:	Forth & Clyde and Union canals (link opening early 2002)

The system comprises at least eight separate canals which together link London with Birmingham, Leicester and Nottingham. Speed limit throughout is 4 mph.

Brentford to Cowley – Waterway Manager, British Waterways, The Toll House, Delamere Terrace, Little Venice, London W2 6ND Tel: 020 7286 6101

Adelaide Dock, Endsleigh Road, Norwood Green, Middlesex
(Adelaide Marine Ltd)

Tel: 020 8571 5678

Type:	shallow concrete slipway and hoist
Suits:	slipway for small powered craft only, hoist for craft up to 70'/21.3m LOA and 10'/3m wide
Availability:	by prior arrangement only
Restrictions:	20 ton weight limit on hoist
Facilities:	diesel, parking for car and trailer(c), water, gas, pump-out, sewage disposal, toilets, boatyard with all facilities; petrol nearby
Licence:	BW licence
Charge:	approx. £25
Directions:	from M4 junction 3 take A312 north, turn right at roundabout into Hayes Road, after canal bridge take immediate right along The Common. At end of road turn left then right into Williams Road, left into Lea Road right into Talbot Road and finally left into Endsleigh Road; site is at the end of Industrial Estate
Waters accessed:	Grand Union Main Line and Paddington Arm, River Thames

Willowtree Marina, West Quay Drive, Yeading, Middx

Tel: 020 8841 6585

Type:	shallow concrete slipway
Suits:	small powered craft except PWC
Availability:	0915 - 1700 daily or by prior arrangement
Restrictions:	bollard to be removed by marina staff before use
Facilities:	diesel, parking for car and trailer(c), telephone, sewage and refuse disposal, water, gas, pump-out, toilets and showers, overnight moorings, launderette, wine bar and restaurant on site; petrol nearby
Licence:	BW licence
Charge:	approx. £12.50
Directions:	from the Hayes bypass A312, take the east exit into Willowtree Lane at the Willowtree roundabout: go past the B & Q warehouse and Tesco Superstore and then turn right into West Quay Drive
Waters accessed:	Grand Union Main Line and Paddington Arm, River Thames

Cowley to Weedon - Waterway Manager, British Waterways, Marsworth Junction, Watery Lane, Marsworth, Tring, Herts HP23 4LZ Tel: 01442 825938

High Line Yachting Ltd. Mansion Lane, Iver, Bucks
Tel: 01753 651496/653151

Type:	shallow concrete slipway
Suits:	craft up to 25'/7.6m LOA
Availability:	tues - sat 0900 - 1800: sun 1100 - 1700; closed mon
Restrictions:	none
Facilities:	diesel on site, petrol nearby, parking for car and trailer, sewage and refuse disposal, water, gas, pump-out, toilet and showers, launderette, chandlery and boatyard including crane
Licence:	BW licence
Charge:	approx. £15
Directions:	follow B470 Langley to Iver road, turning right into Mansion Lane: site is by canal bridge on lock-free 3 mile Slough Arm
Waters accessed:	Grand Union Main Line and Paddington Arm, Rivers Thames, Nene and Soar; Oxford, Stratford on Avon and Birmingham canals

Uxbridge Boat Centre Ltd, Uxbridge Wharf, Waterloo Road, Uxbridge, Middx
Tel: 01895 252019

Type:	shallow concrete slipway
Suits:	powered craft up to approx 20'/6.1m LOA
Availability:	0900 - 1800 tues to sat, 1100 - 1600 sun Feb - Nov
Restrictions:	access is via narrow and sometimes congested streets
Facilities:	diesel on site, petrol nearby, parking for car nearby and for trailer on site, refuse and sewage disposal, water, gas, toilets, chandlery
Licence:	BW licence
Charge:	approx. £17
Directions:	from Uxbridge centre turn onto A4007 towards Slough, after 400m turn left into Waterloo Road; boatyard is on right behind maisonette blocks
Waters accessed:	Grand Union Main Line and Paddington Arm, Rivers Thames, Nene and Soar; Oxford, Stratford on Avon and Birmingham canals

Harefield Marina, Moorhall Road, Harefield, Middx.
Tel: 01895 822036

Type:	concrete slipway
Suits:	small craft
Availability:	0900 - 1730 daily
Restrictions:	none
Facilities:	diesel on site, petrol (1 mile), parking for car and trailer(c), toilets, chandlery and boatyard with crane
Licence:	BW licence
Charge:	yes - on application

Directions: from Denham follow A412 north from the A40 turning right into Moorhall Road
Waters accessed: Grand Union Main Line and Paddington Arm, Rivers Thames, Nene and Soar; Oxford, Stratford on Avon and Birmingham canals

Cowroast Marina, By Cowroast Lock, Tring, Herts

Tel: 01442 823222

Type: shallow concrete slipway
Suits: small powered craft except PWC
Availability: 1000 - 1600 by prior arrangement
Restrictions: weight limit 2 tons
Facilities: diesel, water, parking for car & trailer, gas, pump-out, overnight moorings, chandlery, pub all on site; petrol, toilets & outboard repairs nearby
Licence: BW licence
Charge: approx. £20
Directions: turn off A41onto A4251, turning left across the canal to site by Cowroast Lock
Waters accessed: Grand Union Canal, Rivers Thames, Nene and Soar; Oxford, Stratford on Avon and Birmingham canals

Willowbridge Enterprises, The Marina, Stoke Road, Bletchley, Milton Keynes, Bucks

Tel: 01908 643242 Fax: 01908 366330

Type: crane and mechanical side slip - capacity up to 28 tons
Suits: powered craft (minimum 20'/6.1m LOA)
Availability: 0830 - 1730 daily
Restrictions: launching by crane by prior arrangement and/or side-slip
Facilities: diesel, parking for car and trailer(c), refuse and sewage disposal, water, gas, pump-out, toilets, overnight moorings, chandlery, boatyard, hardstanding DIY
Licence: BW licence
Charge: yes - on application
Directions: turn off the A5 at the roundabout south of Milton Keynes onto the A4146 following signs to Aylesbury and Leighton Buzzard; after crossing canal and roundabout site is on left
Waters accessed: Grand Union Canal, Rivers Thames, Nene and Soar; Oxford, Stratford on Avon and Birmingham canals

Navigation Inn, Cosgrove, Northants

Tel: 01908 543156

Type: concrete slipway
Suits: small powered craft
Availability: by prior arrangement only
Restrictions: may be silted up
Facilities: pub, parking nearby(c); all other facilities at Cosgrove Marina
Licence: BW licence
Charge: donation

Directions:	from M1junction15 follow A508 south, turning left to Cosgrove & Castlethorpe; site is between Cosgrove and Castlethorpe
Waters accessed:	Grand Union Canal, Rivers Thames, Nene and Soar; Oxford, Stratford on Avon and Birmingham canals

Stoke Locks, Stoke Bruerne, Northants

Tel: 01442 825938 (British Waterways office)

Type:	concrete slipway
Suits:	all craft
Availability:	during daylight hours
Restrictions:	gated slipway requires BW key for access
Facilities:	fuel from Yardley Wharf, parking for car and trailer in public car park nearby, toilets in village, chandlers and crane at Yardley Wharf
Licence:	BW licence
Charge:	none
Directions:	leave M1 at junction 15 taking A508 south: site is where road crosses canal between locks 19 and 20
Waters accessed:	Grand Union Canal, Rivers Thames, Nene and Soar; Oxford, Stratford on Avon and Birmingham canals

BW Gayton Yard, Blisworth, Northants

Tel: 01442 825938 (British Waterways office)

Type:	steep concrete slipway
Suits:	craft up to 30'/9.1m LOA
Availability:	during daylight hours: check for availability
Restrictions:	steep slipway
Facilities:	fuel, no parking, telephone, refuse and sewage disposal, water, overnight moorings, toilets, chandlery and boatyard nearby
Licence:	BW licence
Charge:	none
Directions:	from Towcester take A43 north turning left to Tiffield & Gayton; after Tiffield ignore signs to Gayton and follow road over canal; site is on left
Waters accessed:	Grand Union Canal, Rivers Thames, Nene and Soar; Oxford, Stratford on Avon and Birmingham canals

Alvechurch Boat Centre Limited, Gayton Marina, Blisworth, Northants

Tel: 01604 859644

Type:	crane only
Suits:	powered craft up to 30'/9.1m LOA, canoes & rowing dinghies
Availability:	by prior arrangement only
Restrictions:	none
Facilities:	diesel, parking for car & trailer (c), telephone, gas, refuse and sewage disposal, water, overnight moorings, toilets and boat hire on site; chandlery and boatyard nearby
Licence:	BW licence

Charge:	yes - on application
Directions:	from M1 junction15a take A43 N towards Northampton; at first ring road roundabout turn left to Rothersthorpe, turning left at crossroads in village, signposted Milton Malsor and Blisworth; site is after two canal bridges on left
Waters accessed:	Grand Union Canal, Rivers Thames, Nene and Soar, Oxford, Stratford on Avon and Birmingham canals

Whilton Marina, Whilton Locks, Whilton, Daventry, Northants

Tel: 01327 842577

There are launching facilities for narrowboats only at this yard by special arrangement.

GRAND UNION - Leicester Section

This section runs from Norton Junction in the south to the River Trent and is an amalgamation of five separate navigations built in the late eighteenth and early nineteenth centuries. Speed limit is 4 mph.

Norton Junction to Foxton -
Waterway Manager, British Waterways, The Stop House, Braunston, Daventry, Northamptonshire, NN11 7JQ Tel: 01788 890666

Welton Hythe, Welton, Daventry, Northants (Weltonfield Narrowboats)

Tel: 01327 842282

Type:	concrete slipway
Suits:	narrowboats only
Availability:	during daylight hours
Restrictions:	access locked at night
Facilities:	diesel, parking for car (c), telephone, sewage and refuse disposal, water, gas, pump-out, toilets, boatyard, engine repairs
Licence:	BW licence
Charge:	yes - on application
Directions:	site is on the A5, one mile south of the junction with the B4036
Waters accessed:	Grand Union Canal, Rivers Thames, Nene and Soar; Oxford, Stratford on Avon and Birmingham canals

Kilworth Wharf Leisure, Kilworth Wharf, North Kilworth, Leics

Tel:01858 880484

Type:	slipway is steep but level at bottom
Suits:	powered craft up to 20'/6.1m LOA and 6'10"/2.1m wide
Availability:	0900 - 1700 mon to sat, 1000 - 1700 sun
Restrictions:	by prior arrangement only
Facilities:	diesel, parking for car and trailer(c), sewage and refuse disposal, water, gas, pump-out, toilets and showers, overnight moorings, boatyard; petrol nearby
Licence:	BW licence
Charge:	approx. £15

Directions:	turn off M1 at junction 20 taking A4304 east: site is just after leaving North Kilworth
Waters accessed:	Grand Union Canal (Leicester section & main line), Rivers Soar and Trent, Trent & Mersey Canal

Foxton Boat Services, Bottom Lock, Foxton, Market Harborough, Leics

Tel: 0116 2792 285

Type:	shallow concrete slipway
Suits:	small craft up to approx 25'/7.6m LOA
Availability:	0900 - 1100 summer, 0900 - 1700 winter
Restrictions:	by prior arrangement only, narrow access to site
Facilities:	diesel, parking for car and trailer(c), sewage and refuse disposal, water, gas, pump-out, toilets and showers, overnight moorings, chandlery and boatyard with crane, engine repairs, launderette, shop, pub
Licence:	BW licence
Charge:	approx. £5
Directions:	turn off M1 at junction 20 taking A4304 east towards Market Harborough then follow brown signs
Waters accessed:	Grand Union Canal (Leicester section & main line), Rivers Soar and Trent, Trent & Mersey Canal

Foxton to River Trent - Waterway Manager, British Waterways, Sawley Marina, Sawley, Nottinghamshire, NG10 3AE Tel: 0115 973 4278

Raynsway Marina, Pinfold Road, Thurmaston, Leicester

Tel: 0116 2606 166

Type:	steep concrete slipway (1:5)
Suits:	small powered craft
Availability:	0800 - 1700 by prior arrangement
Restrictions:	none
Facilities:	diesel on site, petrol from garage nearby, parking for car and trailer, crane, water, gas, coal, pump-out, toilets, launderette and shop on site; chandlery and outboard repairs nearby,
Licence:	BW licence
Charge:	approx. £5
Directions:	turn off M1 north at junction 21a onto A46 and turn right onto A607 then right down Pinfold road through industrial estate; marina is signposted. From M1 south turn onto A50 at junction 22 then left onto A46 and follow directions for M1 north
Waters accessed:	Grand Union Canal (Leicester section & main line), Rivers Soar and Trent, Trent & Mersey Canal

Nimbus Narrowboats, The Boatyard, Mill Lane, Thurmaston, Leics

Tel: 0116 269 3069

There are launching facilities for narrowboats only at this yard by special arrangement.

L R Harris & Son, Old Junction Boatyard, Meadow Lane, Syston, Leics

Tel: 0116 269 2135

Type:	shallow concrete slipway
Suits:	small powered craft, canoes & rowing dinghies
Availability:	0900 - 1700 daily
Restrictions:	none
Facilities:	diesel, parking for car and trailer, refuse and sewage disposal, water, gas, toilets, chandlery and boatyard, outboard sales, canopies made on site
Licence:	BW licence
Charge:	yes - on application
Directions:	follow A46 and A607 north from Leicester: access to site is from B6670 onto Glebe Way then Meadow Lane is signposted
Waters accessed:	Grand Union Canal (Leicester section & main line), Rivers Soar and Trent, Trent & Mersey Canal

Sileby Mill Boatyard, Mill Lane, Sileby, Leics

Tel: 01509 813583

Type:	shallow concrete slipway, extending underwater
Suits:	all craft
Availability:	during daylight hours by prior arrangement only
Restrictions:	wide trailers may have difficulty getting through gate
Facilities:	diesel, petrol nearby, parking for car and trailer, sewage and refuse disposal, water, gas, pump-out, toilets, showers, overnight moorings, chandlery, boatyard, engine repairs
Licence:	BW licence
Charge:	approx. £10
Directions:	follow A6 north from Leicester turning off towards Sileby at Mountsorrel; site is just off B674
Waters accessed:	Grand Union Canal (Leicester section & main line), Rivers Soar and Trent, Trent & Mersey Canal

East Midlands Boat Services, Willow Moorings, London Road, Kegworth, Leics

Tel/Fax: 01509 672385

Type:	shallow concrete slipway
Suits:	all craft except windsurfers and pwc
Availability:	0900 - 1900 summer only
Restrictions:	access through locked gate, key from office
Facilities:	diesel, parking for car and trailer, sewage disposal, water, gas, toilets, showers, overnight & permanent moorings, chandlery, boatyard, engine repairs
Licence:	BW licence
Charge:	approx. £10 (inc. parking)
Directions:	from M1 junction 24 take A6 towards Loughborough: site is on left 1 mile after Kegworth
Waters accessed:	Grand Union Canal (Leicester section & main line), Rivers Soar and Trent, Trent & Mersey Canal

Red Hill Marina, Red Hill Marine Ltd, Ratcliffe-on-Soar, Nottingham
Tel: 01509 672770

Type:	shallow concrete slipway
Suits:	all craft up to 70'/21.3m LOA
Availability:	by prior arrangement only
Restrictions:	none
Facilities:	diesel, parking for car and trailer, sewage and refuse disposal, water, gas, pump-out, toilets, overnight moorings, chandlery, boatyard, engine repairs; touring caravan site
Licence:	BW licence
Charge:	approx. £7
Directions:	from M1 junction 24 take A453 towards Nottingham; site is on left after 1½ miles
Waters accessed:	Grand Union Canal (Leicester section & main line), Rivers Soar and Trent, Trent & Mersey Canal

GRAND UNION — BW (Midlands Region)

Napton to Camp Hill - Waterway Manager, British Waterways, Brome Hall Lane, Lapworth, Solihull, West Midlands, B94 5RB Tel: 01564 784634

Calcutt Marina, Tomlow Road, Stockton, Nr. Rugby, Warks
Tel: 01926 813757 Fax: 01926 814091

Type:	concrete slipway
Suits:	all craft
Availability:	0900 - 1700 daily by prior arrangement only
Restrictions:	none
Facilities:	diesel, petrol nearby, parking for car and trailer(c), sewage and refuse disposal, water, gas, pump-out, toilets, overnight moorings, chandlery, boatyard, crane by arrangement, engine repairs, hire fleet
Licence:	BW licence
Charge:	yes - on application
Directions:	turn off A425 at Napton taking the Broadwell road: site is on right-hand side, half a mile on from Crossroads Garage
Waters accessed:	Grand Union Canal (main line), Oxford, Stratford on Avon & Birmingham canals, River Thames

GRAND WESTERN CANAL

Devon County Council, County Hall, Exeter EX2 4QQ Tel: 01392 77977

Built from Tiverton to Taunton, the canal was originally24½ miles long. Currently the canal forms part of the Grand Western Canal Country Park and is navigable for just over 11 miles. Speed limit is 4 mph.

Grand Western Canal Country Park, The Moorings, Canal Hill, Tiverton, Devon
Tel: 01884 254072

Type:	shallow grass ramp running down to stones
Suits:	small powered craft, canoes & rowing dinghies
Availability:	during daylight hours

Restrictions: launching can be awkward: use by powered craft is restricted and by prior arrangement only
Facilities: fuel nearby, parking for car and trailer (c), toilets, tea garden
Licence: contact council
Charge: none
Directions: from M5 junction 27 follow North Devon Link road (A361) to Barnstaple; after 5 miles take first Tiverton exit and follow brown signs to canal car park
Waters accessed: Grand Western Canal

GRANTHAM CANAL BW (North East Region)

Waterway Manager, British Waterways, Sawley Marina, Sawley, Nottinghamshire, NG10 3AE Tel: 0115 973 4278

Built from Grantham to the River Trent at Trent Bridge, Nottingham, there are two sections currently navigable for small craft; a 4¼ mile section near Denton from Woolsthorpe to the A1 near Grantham and a 2¼ mile section from Hickling to Long Clawson. Further information from the Grantham Canal Restoration Partnership Tel: 0115 953 1153.

Denton Wharf, Denton, nr Grantham, Lincs

Type: concrete slipway
Suits: all trailable craft
Availability: during daylight hours
Restrictions: slipway is fairly steep
Facilities: parking for car and trailer, picnic site
Licence: BW licence
Charge: none
Directions: from A1 take A607 towards Melton Mowbray, turning right into Denton Village and bearing right again in the village to get to the wharf which is at the end of the farm road by a red brick hump-backed bridge
Waters accessed: Grantham Canal

HUDDERSFIELD BROAD CANAL BW (North West Region)

Waterways Manager, British Waterways, Lock lane, Castleford, West Yorkshire WF10 2LH Tel: 01977 554351

This canal leaves the Calder and Hebble at Cooper Bridge, running for 3½ miles to Huddersfield where it connects with the Huddersfield Narrow Canal. Aspley Basin is the limit of navigation for craft with a beam greater than 7'/2.2m. There is a speed limit of 4 mph.

Aspley Wharf Marina, Aspley Basin, Huddersfield, West Yorks

Tel: 01484 514123 Fax: 01484 431017

Type: steep concrete slipway
Suits: small powered craft, canoes & rowing dinghies
Availability: 0900 - 1700 mon to sat by prior arrangement
Restrictions: BW key required to open Turnbridge Loco Lift Bridge

Facilities:	fuel and parking for cars nearby, sewage and refuse disposal, water, gas, overnight moorings, chandlery and boatyard, boat sales, engine repairs
Licence:	BW licence
Charge:	approx. £10
Directions:	from Huddersfield take A629: site is at first traffic lights
Waters accessed:	Huddersfield Broad and Narrow canals, Calder and Hebble

HUDDERSFIELD NARROW CANAL BW (North West Region)

Waterway Manager, British Waterways, Middle Warehouse, Castle Quay, Manchester M15 4NJ Tel: 0161 819 5847

Built to give a through route across the Pennines, this canal is just under 20 miles long and has the longest tunnel in Britain. The canal re-opened to navigation in May 2001 after a long period of restoration.

Huddersfield University, Wakefield Road, Huddersfield, West Yorks

Tel: 01484 422288 (Estate Department)

Type:	concrete slipway
Suits:	craft up to 20'/6.1m LOA
Availability:	during daylight hours by prior arrangement
Restrictions:	contact Directorate of Estates, Huddersfield University, Queensgate HD1 3DH for permission to launch
Facilities:	fuel, parking for car and trailer(c), toilets
Licence:	BW licence
Charge:	yes - on application
Directions:	site is adjacent A629 Wakefield Road
Waters accessed:	Huddersfield Narrow and Broad canals, Calder and Hebble Navigation, Ashton Canal

Wool Road Car Park, Uppermill, Oldham, Lancs

Type:	concrete slipway (1:6)
Suits:	craft up to 26'/8.1m LOA
Availability:	1000 - 1600 daily
Restrictions:	none
Facilities:	fuel, parking for car and trailer, toilets and telephone all nearby
Licence:	BW licence
Charge:	none
Directions:	turn off A670 Wool Road into public car park
Waters accessed:	Huddersfield Narrow and Broad canals, Calder and Hebble Navigation, Ashton Canal

Slaithwaite, West Yorks

Type:	shallow concrete slipway
Suits:	craft up to 12'/3.6m LOA
Availability:	1000 - 1600 daily
Restrictions:	none
Facilities:	fuel, parking for car and trailer, toilets
Licence:	BW licence

Charge: none
Directions: turn off A62 Manchester Road in town centre into Britannia Road and canal
Waters accessed: Huddersfield Narrow and Broad canals, Calder and Hebble Navigation, Ashton Canal

KENNET AND AVON CANAL — BW (South West Region)

Waterways Manager, British Waterways, The Locks, Bath Road, Devizes, Wilts — Tel: 01380 722859

The canal was built from Newbury to Bath to link two rivers, the Kennet and the Avon. With its connection with the Thames at Reading, the resulting canal became a through route to London but never became very prosperous, falling into disuse in the 1950's. The canal has now been restored throughout, enabling boats to navigate from Reading to Bath and Bristol. There is a speed limit of 4 mph.

Newbury Boat Co, Greenham Island, Mill Lane, Newbury, Berks

Tel: 01635 31672 Fax: 01635 42884 mobile 07990 972133

Type: medium gradient wooden ramp onto gravel
Suits: canal cruisers up to 25'/7.6m LOA
Availability: 0900 - 1700 Apr - Sept, by arrangement only
Restrictions: locked gate to boatyard, booking is essential; boats must have safety certificate and third party insurance for at least £1,000,000
Facilities: diesel on site, petrol nearby, parking for car and trailer(c), toilet, chandlery, sewage and refuse disposal, water, gas, pump-out, overnight moorings all on site
Licence: BW licence
Charge: approx. £15
Directions: leave M4 at junction 13 taking the A339 south and turning left at the second (Sainsbury's) roundabout into Mill Lane: take first left by Greenham Mill housing complex and head for the canal bank and gateway on left
Waters accessed: Kennet & Avon Canal, River Thames, River Avon and Bristol Channel

Pewsey Wharf, Pewsey, Wilts

Tel: 01672 564020 (The Waterfront)

Type: shallow concrete slipway
Suits: craft up to 23'/7m LOA, 9'6"/2.9m width
Availability: 0900 - 1800 daily
Restrictions: none
Facilities: fuel (3 miles), parking for car and trailer, telephone, toilets; pub nearby
Licence: BW licence
Charge: approx. £20
Directions: follow A345 south from Marlborough to Pewsey; site is on left after canal bridge
Waters accessed: Kennet & Avon Canal, River Thames, River Avon and Bristol Channel

Devizes Wharf, Devizes, Wilts

Tel: 01380 724911 (Kennet D.C.)

Type:	steep and narrow concrete slipway
Suits:	craft up to 23'/7m LOA
Availability:	during daylight hours
Restrictions:	can be obstructed by moored craft and parked vehicles
Facilities:	fuel nearby, parking for car and trailer(c), telephone, water, toilets, shop all on site
Licence:	BW licence
Charge:	none
Directions:	follow signs from town centre to wharf
Waters accessed:	Kennet & Avon Canal, River Thames, River Avon and Bristol Channel

Foxhanger Wharf, Lower Foxhangers Farm, Rowde, Devizes, Wilts

Tel: 01380 828254

Type:	shallow gravel hard
Suits:	powered craft up to 23'/7m LOA, canoes & rowing dinghies
Availability:	by prior arrangement only
Restrictions:	access via un-metalled farm track
Facilities:	diesel on site, petrol from Devizes (2 miles), parking for car and trailer(c), water, gas, telephone and toilet nearby, chandlery from Wharfside Chandlery, Devizes (2 miles), repairs on site
Licence:	BW licence
Charge:	approx. £10
Directions:	turn into farm entrance (signed Lower Foxhangers Farm) on north side A361, ½ mile east of junction of A361 and A365 and 2 miles west of Devizes: site is immediately below the Caen Hill flight
Waters accessed:	Kennet & Avon Canal, River Thames, River Avon and Bristol Channel

Tranquil Boats, The Lock House, Semington, Trowbridge, Wilts

Tel: 01380 870654

Type:	shallow concrete slipway
Suits:	small powered craft
Availability:	during daylight hours by arrangement only
Restrictions:	none
Facilities:	fuel (2 miles), parking for car and trailer(c), water
Licence:	BW licence
Charge:	approx. £10
Directions:	from Melksham take A350 south towards Semington; site is on left after bridge over canal
Waters accessed:	Kennet & Avon Canal, River Thames, River Avon and Bristol Channel

Bradford-on-Avon Marina, Trowbridge Road, Widbrook, Bradford-on-Avon

Tel: 01225 864562

Type:	wide shallow concrete slipway
Suits:	all trailed craft: larger boats can be launched by crane
Availability:	0830 - 1700 mon - sat by prior arrangement
Restrictions:	none
Facilities:	diesel, parking for car and trailer, pump-out, refuse and sewage disposal, water, gas, chandlery pub and restaurant
Licence:	BW licence
Charge:	yes - on application
Directions:	from Bradford on Avon take A363 towards Trowbridge; site is on left after bridge over canal
Waters accessed:	Kennet & Avon Canal, River Thames, River Avon and Bristol Channel

Bradford-on-Avon Wharf, Frome Road, Bradford-on-Avon, Wilts

Tel: 01380 722859 (BW South West Region)

Type:	steep concrete slipway
Suits:	craft up to 23'/7m LOA
Availability:	by prior arrangement only
Restrictions:	none
Facilities:	fuel nearby, limited parking for car and trailer(c), telephone, toilets
Licence:	BW licence
Charge:	approx. £5
Directions:	follow the A3109 south from Bradford-on-Avon towards Frome; site is on left after canal bridge
Waters accessed:	Kennet & Avon Canal, River Thames, River Avon and Bristol Channel

Brass Knocker Basin, Monkton Combe, Bath (Somerset Coal Canal Co.)

Tel: 01225 722069

Type:	concrete slipway
Suits:	craft up to 23'/7m LOA and 6'10"/2.1m wide
Availability:	during working hours by prior arrangement only
Restrictions:	stop lock at canal entrance limits boat width
Facilities:	diesel, petrol nearby on A36, parking for car and trailer(c), telephone, refuse and sewage disposal, water, gas, pump-out, toilets and boatyard
Licence:	BW licence
Charge:	yes - on application
Directions:	from Bath take A36 towards Warminster: at Limpley Stoke follow brown signs to Canal Centre; site is on Somerset Coal Canal
Waters accessed:	Kennet & Avon Canal, River Thames, River Avon and Bristol Channel

Waterway Manager, British Waterways, Main Road, Galgate,
Lancaster LA2 0LQ Tel: 01524 751888

Built to improve access from Lancaster to Preston and thence to Wigan and Manchester, the canal is now navigable for just over 42 miles from Preston to Carnforth: the only access to the sea is via the Glasson Branch. It is hoped that the link with the River Ribble will be completed in spring 2002: contact 'British Waterways as above for details. There is a speed limit of 4 mph and a BW key is needed for locks on the canal.

Moons Bridge Marina, Hollowforth Lane, Woodplumpton, Preston, Lancs
Tel: 01772 690627

Type:	shallow concrete slipway
Suits:	small powered craft
Availability:	0900 - 1700 by prior arrangement only
Restrictions:	none
Facilities:	diesel on site, petrol nearby, parking for car and trailer(c), refuse and sewage disposal, water, gas, chandlery, boat-yard with crane and winch, engine repairs
Licence:	BW licence
Charge:	approx. £10
Directions:	from M6 junction 32 follow A6 to Broughton cross roads (traffic lights), turn left onto B5269 after 1½ miles turn right at T-junction then right again into Hollowforth Lane; site is on right after 500m
Waters accessed:	Lancaster Canal, River Lune and open sea via Glasson Branch and Glasson Dock

Marina Park, Canal Wharf, Galgate, Lancs
Tel: 01524 751368

Type:	concrete slipway
Suits:	craft up to 60'/18.3m LOA
Availability:	during working hours by prior arrangement
Restrictions:	none
Facilities:	fuel, parking for car and trailer(c), refuse and sewage disposal, water, gas, toilets and showers, chandlery, boatyard with crane and winch
Licence:	BW licence
Charge:	yes - on application
Directions:	leave M6 at junction 33 taking A6 towards Lancaster
Waters accessed:	Lancaster Canal, Glasson Branch, River Lune and sea

Glasson Basin Yacht Co, Glasson Dock, Lancs
Tel: 01524 751491

Type:	concrete slipway (1:12)
Suits:	all craft
Availability:	0900 - 1700 mon to fri by prior arrangement only

Restrictions:	locks on Glasson Branch take boats up to 72'/21.9m LOA: 24 hours notice is required to lock out into Glasson Dock Tel: 01524 751566
Facilities:	fuel, parking for car and trailer(c), refuse and sewage disposal, water, gas, toilets and showers, moorings, chandlery, boatyard with crane and winch, engine repairs
Licence:	BW licence
Charge:	approx. £25
Directions:	from Lancaster follow A588 south, turning right onto B5290 after Conder Green
Waters accessed:	Lancaster Canal, River Lune and open sea via Glasson Dock

Nu-Way Acorn, Lundsfield, Carnforth, Lancs

Tel: 01524 734457

Type:	concrete slipway
Suits:	all powered craft
Availability:	during working hours by prior arrangement
Restrictions:	none
Facilities:	diesel, parking for car and trailer(c), telephone, refuse disposal, overnight moorings, boatyard, engine repairs
Licence:	BW licence
Charge:	yes - on application
Directions:	turn off M6 at junction 35, taking A6 to Carnforth
Waters accessed:	Lancaster Canal, River Lune and open sea via Glasson Branch and Glasson Dock

LEE AND STORT NAVIGATION — BW (South East Region)

Waterway Manager, British Waterways, Enfield Lock, South Ordnance Road, Enfield, Middx EN3 6JG Tel: 01992 764626 Fax: 01992 788226

The River Lee (Lea) is navigable for almost 28 miles from Limehouse Basin to Hertford. The river can also be entered from Bow Creek via Bow Locks or from the Regent's Canal via the Hertford Union Canal. The junction with the River Stort, which is canalised for nearly 14 miles to Bishop's Stortford, is at Fielde's Weir. Together these make over 42 miles of cruising waterway. There is a speed limit of 4 mph.

Lee Valley Marina, Springfield, Spring Hill, Clapton, London

Tel: 020 8806 1717

Type:	concrete slipway and boat lift
Suits:	craft up to 36'/11m LOA
Availability:	0835 - 1700 daily by prior arrangement only
Restrictions:	access via unmade track
Facilities:	diesel, parking for car and trailer(c), telephone, sewage and refuse disposal, water, gas, pump-out, toilet and showers, overnight moorings, boatyard with boat lift up to 25'/7.6m LOA
Licence:	BW licence
Charge:	yes - on application

Directions:	turn off A104 Lea Bridge Road in Leyton: marina is on east bank
Waters accessed:	River Thames and canal network

Hazlemere Marina, High Bridge Street, Waltham Abbey, Essex

Tel:01992 764626

Type:	concrete slipway
Suits:	craft up to 24'/7.3m LOA and 8'/2.4m beam
Availability:	by prior arrangement only
Restrictions:	none
Facilities:	diesel on site, petrol nearby, parking for car and trailer(c), telephone, sewage and refuse disposal, pump-out, water, toilets, overnight moorings, cafe
Licence:	BW licence
Charge:	approx. £10
Directions:	turn off M25 at junction 26 following A121 west: access to site is from High Bridge Street
Waters accessed:	River Thames and canal network

Lee Valley Marina, South Street, Stanstead Abbots, Herts

Tel: 01920 870499

Type:	fairly steep concrete slipway
Suits:	craft up to 25'/7.6m LOA with max 5'/1.5m draught
Availability:	0900 - 1630 daily
Restrictions:	locked barrier to site
Facilities:	diesel on site, petrol (1 mile), parking for car and trailer (c for long term parking), telephone, refuse and sewage disposal, water, pump-out, toilets and showers, overnight moorings, chandlery, boatyard with crane, engine repairs: cafe, pubs & shops nearby
Licence:	BW licence
Charge:	approx. £9
Directions:	from M25 junction25 follow A10 north and take A414 towards Harlow. At roundabout turn onto B181 to Stanstead Abbots; South Street is off High Street
Waters accessed:	River Thames and canal network

LEEDS AND LIVERPOOL CANAL BW (North West Region)

West (Greenberfield to Liverpool) - Waterway Manager, British Waterways, Pottery Road, Wigan, Lancs WN3 5AA Tel: 01942 242239

East (Greenberfield to Leeds) - Waterway Manager, British Waterways, Dobson Lock, Apperley Bridge, Bradford, West Yorks BD10 OPY Tel: 01274 611303

The longest canal built by one company, this canal is 127 miles long. It connects Leeds to the River Mersey at Liverpool via the Stanley Dock Branch, the Ribble Estuary at Tarleton via the Rufford Branch and the Bridgewater Canal via the Leigh Branch. In Leeds the canal connects with the Aire and Calder Navigation at River Lock. Speed limit is 4 mph.

The Lathom Slipway, 48 Crabtree Lane, Burscough, Lancs

Tel: 01704 897767

Type:	shallow concrete slipway
Suits:	craft up to 25'/7.6m LOA and 9'/2.7m wide
Availability:	at all times by prior arrangement only
Restrictions:	none
Facilities:	parking for car and trailer, toilets, overnight moorings; diesel, chandlery, water, gas from Lathom Marine adjacent
Licence:	BW licence
Charge:	approx. £5
Directions:	from Ormskirk follow A59 turning left on south side of canal into Higgans Lane, turning fourth right into Crabtree Lane: site is by bridge 32
Waters accessed:	Leeds & Liverpool, Aire and Calder and Bridgewater canals, Rivers Mersey and Douglas/Ribble

James Mayor, The Boatyard, Tarleton, Nr. Preston, Lancs

Tel: 01772 812250

Suits:	all craft (slipway up to 90'/27.4m LOA)
Availability:	during daylight hours
Restrictions:	Rufford Branch can only be entered or left via Tarleton Lock at HW
Facilities:	diesel, parking for car and trailer, telephone, sewage and refuse disposal, water, gas, pump-out, toilets and showers, overnight moorings, chandlery, boatyard, 3-ton crane and winch, engine repairs
Licence:	BW licence for canal, no licence for river
Charge:	yes - on application
Directions:	from junction of A59 and A565 take Church Road through village then down Plox Brow and along canal bank: site is on Rufford Branch
Waters accessed:	Leeds and Liverpool Canal and River Douglas via Tarleton Lock

White Bear Marina, Park Road, Adlington, Nr. Chorley, Lancs

Tel: 01257 481054 Fax: 01257 474604

Type:	concrete slipway
Suits:	craft up to 45'/13.7m LOA and 10'/3m wide

Availability:	0900 - 1200, 1300 - 1800 mon - fri, 1000 - 1800 sat - sun
Restrictions:	none
Facilities:	fuel, parking for car and trailer(c), telephone, refuse and sewage disposal, water, gas, pump-out, toilets and showers, overnight moorings, cafe, laundry, chandlery, boatyard, engine repairs
Licence:	BW licence available on site
Charge:	yes - on application
Directions:	leave M61 northbound at junction 6 taking A6 north for 2 miles to Adlington or leave M6 at junction 27 following signs to Standish, then Chorley, then A6 towards Manchester, turning off in Adlington
Waters accessed:	Rivers Mersey and Douglas/Ribble, Aire and Calder and Bridgewater canals

British Waterways, Botany Bay, Chorley, Lancs

Tel: 01282 456978

Type:	concrete slipway
Suits:	craft up to 25'/7.6m LOA
Availability:	by prior arrangement only
Restrictions:	none
Facilities:	refuse and sewage disposal, water, overnight moorings
Licence:	BW licence
Charge:	approx £50
Directions:	from M61 junction 8 take A674 towards Wheelton turning right onto B6228; site is opposite 'Botany Bay Village' by bridge 78a
Waters accessed:	Leeds & Liverpool, Aire and Calder and Bridgewater canals; Rivers Mersey and Douglas/Ribble

Hapton Boatyard, Simpson Street, Hapton, Burnley, Lancs

Tel: 01282 773178

Type:	launching by 15 ton mobile crane only
Suits:	larger craft only
Availability:	by prior arrangement only
Restrictions:	no slipway
Facilities:	diesel, parking for car & trailer (c), water, gas, overnight moorings, chandlery, boatyard, engine repairs
Licence:	BW licence
Charge:	yes - on application
Directions:	turn off the M65 at junction 8 taking the A56 and A679
Waters accessed:	Leeds & Liverpool, Aire and Calder and Bridgewater canals; Rivers Mersey and Douglas/Ribble

Silsden Boats, The Wharf, Elliott street, Silsden, Nr. Keighley, West Yorks

Tel: 01535 653675

Type:	steep concrete slipway
Suits:	craft up to 30'/9.1m LOA and 8'/2.4m wide
Availability:	by prior arrangement only

Facilities:	diesel on site, petrol nearby, parking for car and trailer by arrangement, toilet, refuse disposal, water, gas, pump-out, crane by arrangement
Licence:	BW licence
Charge:	approx. £20
Directions:	turn off A629 north of Keighley onto the A6034: site is approached via Elliott Street
Waters accessed:	Leeds & Liverpool, Aire and Calder and Bridgewater canals; Rivers Mersey and Douglas/Ribble

Hainsworths Boatyard, Fairfax Road, Bingley, West Yorks

Tel: 01274 565925

Type:	medium concrete slipway
Suits:	small powered craft
Availability:	0830 - 2200 summer, 0830 - 1700 winter
Restrictions:	locked barrier outside opening times
Facilities:	fuel nearby, parking for car and trailer(c), telephone, water, gas, pump-out, toilets, overnight moorings,chandlery, boatyard
Licence:	BW licence
Charge:	approx. £16
Directions:	approach on A650 Keighley/Bradford road, turning at main traffic lights in Bingley up Park Road towards Eldwick. After half a mile turn left into Hall Bank Drive, left at end into Beck Lane and straight over roundabout: yard is at very end on left just above Five Rise Locks
Waters accessed:	Leeds & Liverpool, Aire and Calder and Bridgewater canals; Rivers Mersey and Douglas/Ribble

Rodley Boat Centre, Canal Wharf, Canal Road, Rodley, Leeds, West Yorks

Tel: 0113 257 6132

Type:	steep concrete slipway
Suits:	all craft
Availability:	0900 - dusk daily by prior arrangement
Restrictions:	fairly steep slipway
Facilities:	fuel, parking for car and trailer (c), refuse and sewage disposal, water, gas, pump-out, toilets, overnight moorings, chandlery, boatyard
Licence:	BW licence
Charge:	yes - on application
Directions:	site is off Leeds Outer Ring Road and adjacent A657, by bridge 216A
Waters accessed:	Leeds & Liverpool, Aire and Calder and Bridgewater canals; Rivers Mersey and Douglas/Ribble

Fallwood Marina, Pollard Lane, Bramley, Leeds, West Yorks

Tel: 0113 258 1074

Type:	steep concrete slipway
Suits:	all craft
Availability:	0900 - 1730 mon - fri, 1000 - 1600 sat and sun, closed tues
Restrictions:	steep slipway

Facilities:	diesel, parking for car and trailer(c), refuse and sewage disposal, water, gas, toilets, overnight moorings, boatyard, crane
Licence:	BW licence
Charge:	yes - on application
Directions:	turn off ring road onto A657 Leeds to Bradford road
Waters accessed:	Leeds & Liverpool, Aire and Calder and Bridgewater canals; Rivers Mersey and Douglas/Ribble

Aire Valley Marina, Redcote Lane, Kirkstall, Leeds, West Yorks

Tel: 0113 279 8997

Type:	wide shallow concrete slip
Suits:	all craft up to 25'/7.6m LOA
Availability:	0900 - 1700 daily
Restrictions:	none
Facilities:	diesel, parking for car and trailer(c over 24hrs), sewage disposal, pump-out, water, gas, showers, engine repairs on site, shops etc. all nearby
Licence:	BW licence
Charge:	approx.£10
Directions:	from Leeds follow A65 west turning left into Redcote Lane after approx. 2 miles
Waters accessed:	Leeds & Liverpool, Aire and Calder and Bridgewater canals; Rivers Mersey and Douglas/Ribble

LLANGOLLEN CANAL — BW (North West Region)

Waterway Manager, British Waterways, Canal Office, Birch Road, Ellesmere, Shropshire SY12 9AA — Tel: 01691 622549

One of the most popular cruising canals with its great aqueducts at Chirk and Pontcsyllte, it was originally planned to connect the Mersey to the Severn but is now navigable for 46 miles from Llantisilio to Hurleston Junction where it connects with the Shropshire Union Canal. There is a speed limit of 4 mph.

Whixall Marina, Alders Lane, Whixall, Shropshire

Tel: 01948 880420/540

Type:	concrete slipway
Suits:	small powered craft, canoes and rowing dinghies
Availability:	0900 - 1600 daily by prior arrangement
Restrictions:	locked entrance out of opening hours
Facilities:	diesel, parking for car and trailer (c), sewage and refuse disposal, water, gas, pump-out, toilets, overnight moorings, chandlery
Licence:	BW licence
Charge:	yes - on application
Directions:	phone for directions
Waters accessed:	Llangollen Canal

Blackwater Meadow Marina, Birch Road, Ellesmere, Shropshire
Tel: 01691 624391

Type:	shallow becoming steep concrete slipway
Suits:	small powered craft
Availability:	by prior arrangement only
Restrictions:	none
Facilities:	diesel on site, petrol nearby, parking for car, sewage and refuse disposal, water, gas, pump-out, toilets, overnight moorings, chandlery, boatyard
Licence:	BW licence
Charge:	approx. £10
Directions:	from Shrewsbury take A528 Wrexham road or from Oswestry take A495 to Ellesmere
Waters accessed:	Llangollen Canal

Maestermyn Marine Ltd, Ellesmere Road, Whittington, Oswestry, Shropshire
Tel: 01691 662424

Type:	concrete slipway
Suits:	small craft
Availability:	during working hours by prior arrangement
Restrictions:	none
Facilities:	diesel, petrol (½ mile), parking for car and trailer, telephone, sewage and refuse disposal, water, gas, pump-out, toilets, overnight moorings, chandlery and boatyard
Licence:	BW licence
Charge:	yes - on application
Directions:	turn off the A5 north-east of Oswestry onto the A495: site is adjacent to road between Whittington and Ellesmere
Waters accessed:	Llangollen Canal

MACCLESFIELD CANAL — BW (North West Region)

Waterway Manager, British Waterways, Red Bull Yard, Congleton Road South, Church Lawton, Stoke on Trent ST7 3AP Tel: 01782 785703

Built as an alternative link between the Midlands and Manchester, this 28 mile long canal links the Peak Forest Canal and the Trent and Mersey Canal. It now forms part of the 100 mile "Cheshire Ring" canal circuit. There is a speed limit of 4 mph.

Red Bull Services, Red Bull Basin, Church Lawton, Stoke on Trent, Staffs
Tel: 01782 779033

Type:	shallow concrete slipway
Suits:	small powered craft, canoes and rowing dinghies
Availability:	by prior arrangement
Restrictions:	none
Facilities:	diesel, parking for car and trailer(c), toilets, sewage and refuse disposal, water, gas, pump-out, shop, chandlery, repairs
Licence:	BW licence

Charge:	approx. £30
Directions:	from M6 junctiont 16 take A500 towards Stoke and after three miles take A34 towards Congleton through village of Butt Lane; site is on right before entrance to Red Bull pub
Waters accessed:	Macclesfield, Trent and Mersey and Peak Forest canals

Macclesfield Canal Centre Ltd, Brook Street, Macclesfield, Cheshire

Tel:01625 420042

Type:	shallow concrete slipway
Suits:	craft up to 23'/7m LOA and with 2'10"/0.85m draught and 6'10"/2.1m beam
Availability:	0900 - 1800 by prior arrangement
Restrictions:	none
Facilities:	diesel, parking for car and trailer (c long-term), sewage and refuse disposal, water, gas, coal, pump-out, toilets and showers, overnight moorings, shop, chandlery; petrol nearby
Licence:	BW licence
Charge:	approx. £10 (canoes free)
Directions:	leave M6 at junction 17 taking A534, A54 and A523
Waters accessed:	Macclesfield, Trent and Mersey and Peak Forest canals

Lyme View Marina, Wood Lane East, Adlington, Macclesfield, Cheshire

Tel: 01625 858176

Type:	shallow concrete slipway
Suits:	small powered craft
Availability:	daily during working hours
Restrictions:	7 knot speed limit in marina
Facilities:	diesel, parking for car and trailer, sewage and refuse disposal, water, gas, pump-out, toilets and showers, cafe, shop, day boat hire
Licence:	BW licence
Charge:	approx. £10
Directions:	from A523 north of Macclesfield, turn right opposite Little Chef; follow Steel Lane for ¾ mile then turn left at T-junction and follow road over crossroads to marina
Waters accessed:	Macclesfield, Trent and Mersey and Peak Forest canals

Tonbridge District Office, Medway House, Powder Mill Lane, Leigh, Tonbridge, Kent TN11 9AS Tel: 01732 838858

The River Medway Navigation gives access to 19 miles of the fresh water river above its tidal limit at Allington Lock and to the tidal river and Thames Estuary below. The lock is accessible from 3 hours before to 2 hours after HW Tel: 01622 752864. All vessels using the navigation must be registered and there is a speed limit of 5 knots.

Dragons Health & Fitness Club, Record Tennis Centre, St. Peter's Street, Maidstone, Kent

Tel: 01622 681987

Type:	concrete slipway
Suits:	small craft
Availability:	during daylight hours
Restrictions:	none
Facilities:	fuel, limited parking for car and trailer(c), water, gas from Allington Marina
Licence:	EA licence available on site
Charge:	approx. £8 or £3 for canoe
Directions:	turn down St. Peter's Street under the arch at the bottom of the hill
Waters accessed:	River Medway and Thames Estuary via Allington Lock

Tovil Bridge Boatyard, Beaconsfield Road, Tovil, Maidstone, Kent

Tel: 01622 686341

Type:	concrete slipway
Suits:	craft up to 20'/6.1m LOA
Availability:	during working hours
Restrictions:	none
Facilities:	diesel, parking for car and trailer, water, boatyard, engine repairs
Licence:	EA licence available from Allington Lock or Yalding Lift Bridge Depot
Charge:	approx. £5
Directions:	turn off the A26 at Teston onto the B2010, turning left in Tovil into Church Street and Wharfe Road and right into Beaconsfield Road
Waters accessed:	River Medway and Thames Estuary via Allington Lock

Medway Wharf Marina, Bow Bridge, Wateringbury, Kent

Tel: 01622 813927

Type:	steep slipway
Suits:	small powered craft, canoes and rowing dinghies
Availability:	daily
Restrictions:	steep slipway: launching by yard staff if required
Facilities:	diesel, parking for car and trailer, gas, toilets, moorings, chandlery, engine repairs, boatyard, crane: petrol nearby
Licence:	EA licence
Charge:	approx. £12

Directions: follow A26 from Maidstone turning left at traffic lights in Wateringbury: turn left half a mile down hill going over bridge and then take first right

Waters accessed: River Medway and Thames Estuary via Allington Lock

Hampstead Slipway, Hampstead Lock, Yalding, Kent

Tel: 01732 838858/ 01622 814319

Type: steep concrete slipway

Suits: craft up to 25'/7.6m LOA

Availability: 0900, 1200 &1500 mon - fri all year, & sat & sun Oct - Mar; 0900 - 1 hour before sunset sat, sun and Bank Holidays Apr - Oct

Restrictions: launch by arrangement with lock-keeper at lifting bridge: access is difficult and parking close by prohibited

Facilities: parking (½ mile), chandlery and boatyard available locally; water, refuse and sewage facilities available at EA depot

Licence: EA licence available from lock-keeper at Yalding Lift Bridge Depot

Charge: approx. £5

Directions: turn off B2015 at Nettlestead Green into Station Road, then on to Hampstead Lane and over the level crossing: site entrance is on left opposite the entrance to the Zeneca factory

Waters accessed: River Medway and Thames Estuary via Allington Lock

Lower Castle Field, The Slade,Tonbridge, Kent

Tel: 01732 770929 (Tonbridge Castle TIC)

Type: steep concrete slipway

Suits: small powered craft, canoes and rowing dinghues

Availability: during daylight hours

Restrictions: access is via narrow and often congested streets and the car park has a height restriction of 6'/1.8m

Facilities: fuel nearby, parking for car and trailer(c), telephone, toilets nearby, sewage and refuse disposal at Town Lock

Licence: EA licence available from TIC at Castle

Charge: none

Directions: follow A26 into Tonbridge High Street, turning left after the castle, following signs to swimming pool, into Castle Street and the Slade to riverside car park

Waters accessed: River Medway and Thames Estuary via Allington Lock

MIDDLE LEVEL NAVIGATIONS **Middle Level Commissioners**

Middle Level Offices, Dartford Road, March, Cambs PE15 8AF
Tel: 01354 53232

This complex system of channels which occupies much of the lowland between the Rivers Nene and Ouse dates from the mid 17th century. Pleasure craft are not required to pay a licence fee but visitors should register with the lock-keeper at Stanground or Salters Lode when entering the system. There is a maximum speed limit of 5 mph with the exception of Kings Dyke and Well Creek, where the limit is 4 mph.

C T Fox, 10, Marina Drive, March, Cambs
Tel: 01354 52770

Type:	concrete slipway
Suits:	all craft
Availability:	during working hours by arrangement only
Restrictions:	no pwc
Facilities:	diesel, parking for car and trailer, toilets, chandlery, water, gas, boatyard; petrol nearby
Licence:	none but registration required - see above
Charge:	approx. £7.50
Directions:	leave the A141 at March roundabout taking Turves exit and bearing left into Marina Drive
Waters accessed:	Middle Levels, Rivers Nene and Great Ouse

Bill Fen Marina, Mill Drove, Ramsey, Huntingdon PE17 1RD
Tel: 01487 813621

Type:	concrete slipway
Suits:	small craft
Availability:	during opening hours only
Restrictions:	none
Facilities:	diesel, parking by arrangement, water, toilets, limited chandlery
Licence:	none but registration required - see above
Charge:	approx. £11
Directions:	phone for directions
Waters accessed:	Middle Levels, Rivers Nene and Great Ouse

MONMOUTHSHIRE AND BRECON CANAL

BW (South West Region)

Waterway Manager, British Waterways, The Wharf, Govilon, Abergavenny, Gwent NP7 9NY Tel: 01873 830328

There are navigable lengths from Pontypool to Brecon, once the original Brecon and Abergavenny Canal (just over 33 miles) and on the Crumlin Arm from Cwmcarn to the outskirts of Risca (just over 2 miles). There is a speed limit of 3 mph.

Pontymoile Basin, Pontypool, Torfaen, Gwent

Tel: 07970 548810 Fax: 01495 774473

Type:	concrete slipway
Suits:	small powered craft, canoes and rowing dinghies
Availability:	phone for details
Restrictions:	narrow road leading to locked gates
Facilities:	parking for car & trailer, toilet, refuse and sewage disposal, water, visitor moorings, tea room on site; petrol, chandlery and outboard repairs nearby
Licence:	BW licence
Charge:	yes - on application
Directions:	leave M4 at junction 25a taking A4042 north and turning off to Pontypool: site is north of canal bridge 52
Waters accessed:	Monmouthshire and Brecon Canal

Goytre Wharf, Llanover, Abergavenny, Monmouthshire

Tel/Fax: 01873 881069

Type:	concrete slipway
Suits:	small powered craft, canoes and rowing dinghies
Availability:	0800 - 1700 daily
Restrictions:	BW security key required
Facilities:	diesel, parking for car and trailer(c), sewage and refuse disposal, water, gas, pump-out, toilets and showers, visitor moorings, chandlery, boatyard, engine repairs, tea room
Licence:	BW licence (available on site)
Charge:	none
Directions:	leave M4 at junction 25a taking A4042 north, turning left at Mamhilad roundabout (Du Pont factory on left); site is on right after approx. 3 miles
Waters accessed:	Monmouthshire and Brecon canal

Crumlin Arm

Pontywaun Slipway, Halls Road Terrace, Crosskeys, Gwent

Tel: 01495 271177 (Tony Edwards) or 029 2088 8681 (Chris Morgan) - keyholders

Type:	steep concrete slipway to IWA specification
Suits:	craft up to 23'/7mLOA
Availability:	by prior arrangement only
Restrictions:	locked barrier, key holders as above

Facilities:	fuel nearby, parking for car & trailer on site, pub and shop nearby
Licence:	contact keyholders
Charge:	contact keyholders
Directions:	from M4 junction 28 (signposted Risca), follow A467 north for 7 miles then through Pontywaun village; cross canal bridge and turn immediate left into Halls Road Terrace; site is 150m on left
Waters accessed:	Crumlin Arm (2 miles) of Montmouthshire & Brecon Canal

MONTGOMERY CANAL — BW (North West Region)

Waterway Manager, British Waterways, Birch Road, Ellesmere, Shropshire SY12 9AA — Tel: 01691 622549

This canal was planned to run northwards from Newtown and joined the Llangollen Canal at Frankton Junction. Part of the canal has been restored but there are serious obstacles to complete restoration. Speed limit is 4 mph.

Pool Quay, Wern, Powys

Type:	concrete slipway
Suits:	small craft
Availability:	during daylight hours
Restrictions:	approach via narrow road
Facilities:	fuel nearby, parking for car and trailer
Licence:	purchase a BW sanitary key to gain access
Charge:	none
Directions:	turn off A483 north of Welshpool and over the old railway crossing: site is below Bugeddin Locks
Waters accessed:	Montgomery Canal

Town Quay Slipway, Smithfield Car Park, Welshpool, Powys

Type:	concrete slipway
Suits:	small powered craft, canoes and rowing dinghies
Availability:	during daylight hours
Restrictions:	access may be blocked by parked vehicles
Facilities:	fuel nearby, parking for car and trailer(c), overnight moorings, sewage disposal; shops nearby
Licence:	purchase BW sanitary key to gain access
Charge:	none
Directions:	turn off A483 by Spar shop into Church Street: site is in car park
Waters accessed:	Montgomery Canal

Kingfisher House, Goldhay Way, Orton Goldhay, Peterborough PE2 OZR
Tel: 01733 371811

The river is tidal for 25 miles as far as the Dog-in-a-Doublet lock and sluice, five miles below Peterborough and is controlled by the Port of Wisbech Authority. The lock is open daily from 0730 - sunset: it is advisable to telephone the lock-keeper in advance Tel: 01733 202219 to make arrangements. Above the lock, the river is navigable to Northampton and thence to the Grand Union Canal via the Northampton Branch. Entry to the Middle Levels and thence the River Ouse and the sea is via Stanground Lock. There is a speed limit of 5 mph with a derestricted stretch of water one mile downstream of Peterborough.

Billing Aquadrome Ltd. Crow Lane, Great Billing, Northampton, Northants
Tel: 01604 408312

Type: concrete slipway
Suits: small powered craft, canoes and rowing dinghies
Availability: 1000 - 1700 daily
Restrictions: none
Facilities: fuel nearby, parking for car and trailer(c), telephone, sewage and refuse disposal, water, gas, toilets and showers, overnight moorings, chandlery, boatyard, engine repairs
Licence: EA licence
Charge: approx. £15
Directions: turn off M1 at junction 16, taking the A45 east and following brown signs
Waters accessed: River Nene, Grand Union Canal, River Ouse, North Sea

Wellingborough Upper Lock, Wellingborough, Northants
Tel: 01536 517721

Type: concrete slipway
Suits: all trailable craft
Availability: during daylight hours
Restrictions: access is difficult with a fairly tight turn
Facilities: no parking on site, water, toilets nearby
Licence: EA licence
Charge: none
Directions: follow A45 east from Northampton, turning off onto A509: site is downstream of lock and access is via Turnells Mill Lane
Waters accessed: River Nene, Grand Union Canal, River Ouse, North Sea

Mill Marina, Midland Road, Thrapston, Northants
Tel: 01832 732850

Type: shallow concrete slipway with metal grooves
Suits: small powered craft up to 22'/6.7m LOA, canoes and rowing dinghies
Availability: 0900 - 1800 by prior arrangement

Restrictions: maximum weight 3 tons, maximum width 8'/2.4m
Facilities: petrol nearby, parking for car and trailer(c), telephone, sewage and refuse disposal, water, gas, toilets and showers, overnight moorings, caravan site, bar
Licence: EA licence
Charge: approx. £9
Directions: follow A14 west from Huntingdon, taking A605 north towards Thrapston then follow caravan signs
Waters accessed: River Nene, Grand Union Canal, River Ouse, North Sea

Oundle Marina, Barnwell Road, Oundle, Northants

Tel: 01832 272762

Type: shallow concrete slipway
Suits: all small craft
Availability: 0900 - 1700 (closed wed) or by arrangement
Restrictions: none
Facilities: fuel, parking for car and trailer(c), sewage and refuse disposal, water, gas, toilets, and showers, chandlery, boatyard with crane and gantry
Licence: EA licence
Charge: approx. £9
Directions: follow A605 from A1 towards Oundle, turning off to right
Waters accessed: River Nene, Grand Union Canal, River Ouse, North Sea

Yarwell Mill Caravan Park, Yarwell, Peterborough, Cambs

Tel: 01780 782247

Type: concrete slipway
Suits: trailable craft up to 28'/8.5m LOA
Availability: during daylight hours
Restrictions: none
Facilities: parking for car and trailer, toilets and showers, pub nearby
Licence: EA licence
Charge: yes - on application
Directions: turn off A1 west of Peterborough at A47 intersection, following signs to Yarwell at Wansford Church
Waters accessed: River Nene, Grand Union Canal, River Ouse, North Sea

Potters Way, Fengate, Peterborough, Cambs

Tel: 01733 742541/742537

Type: concrete slipway
Suits: craft up to 20'/6.1m LOA
Availability: during daylight hours
Restrictions: barrier restricts height to 7'/2.1m: key to barrier is available from Leisure and Recreation Dept. of City Council Tel: 01733 742530
Facilities: parking for car and trailer(c): fuel, chandlery etc. from Peterborough Boating Centre, 73 North Street
Licence: EA licence
Charge: none

Directions:	turn into Potters Way in City Centre: access is through car park
Waters accessed:	River Nene, Grand Union Canal, River Ouse, North Sea

GREAT OUSE RIVER — EA (Anglian Region)

Kingfisher House, Goldhay Way, Orton Goldhay, Peterborough PE2 OZR
Tel: 01733 371811

The river is navigable from Bedford to Denver Sluice. The navigation authority for the lower reaches of the river and seaward approaches to King's Lynn is the King's Lynn Conservancy Board. Access to the sea is via Denver Sluice and to the Middle Levels and thence the River Nene via Stanground Sluice. There is a speed limit of 6 knots unless otherwise specified.

Priory Marina Ltd, Barkers Lane, Bedford

Tel:01234 351931

Type:	concrete slipway
Suits:	small craft up to 23'/7m
Availability:	0930 - 1730 daily
Restrictions:	none
Facilities:	fuel, parking for car and trailer, refuse and sewage disposal, pump-out, gas, water, toilets and showers, crane, chandlery, engine repairs, launderette, boatyard, moorings; pub nearby
Licence:	EA licence
Charge:	approx. £5
Directions:	from A1 follow A421 towards Bedford town centre; turn left following signs to Priory Park and then marina
Waters accessed:	River Great Ouse, North Sea, Middle Levels, River Nene

Crosshall Marine, Crosshall Road, St. Neots, Cambs

Tel: 01480 472763

Type:	shallow concrete slipway
Suits:	small craft only
Availability:	0900 - 1930 daily in summer: 0900 - 1730 in winter
Restrictions:	gate access restricts width to 7'4"/2.2m
Facilities:	diesel, parking for car and trailer, water, gas, toilets and showers, overnight moorings, brokerage, chandlery, boatyard; petrol nearby
Licence:	EA licence
Charge:	yes - on application
Directions:	from St Neots take B1048 west and follow signs to St Neots Golf Club: access is through club car park
Waters accessed:	River Great Ouse, North Sea, Middle Levels, River Nene

Buckden Marina, Mill Road, Buckden, Huntingdon, Cambs

Tel: 01480 810355

Type:	shallow concrete slipway
Suits:	small powered craft
Availability:	at all times

Restrictions:	none
Facilities:	fuel, parking for car and trailer, refuse and sewage disposal, pump-out, water, gas, toilets, showers, telephone, launderette, overnight moorings, bar and engine repairs
Licence:	EA licence
Charge:	approx. £10
Directions:	from A1 north of St Neots turn east to Buckden village, turning left by Lion Hotel: site is on left approx. 1 mile below Offord Lock
Waters accessed:	River Great Ouse, North Sea, Middle Levels, River Nene

Hartford Road Car Park, Huntingdon, Cambs

Type:	shallow concrete slipway
Suits:	craft up to 20'/6.1m LOA
Availability:	during daylight hours
Restrictions:	sharp drop at end of slipway
Facilities:	fuel nearby, parking for car and trailer
Licence:	EA licence
Charge:	none
Directions:	follow ring road round town, turning off to follow signs to St. Ives: after 50m, cross over into car park by river; site is downstream of Purvis Marine
Waters accessed:	River Great Ouse, North Sea, Middle Levels, River Nene

Hartford Marina, Banks End, Wyton, Huntingdon, Cambs

Tel: 01480 454677

Type:	shallow concrete slipway
Suits:	craft up to 60'/18.3m with less than 3'/0.9m draught
Availability:	0800 - 1700 daily
Restrictions:	none
Facilities:	fuel, parking for car and trailer(c), telephone, refuse and sewage disposal, water, gas, toilets and showers, overnight moorings, chandlery, boatyard with crane, engine repairs, restaurant and caravan site
Licence:	EA licence
Charge:	approx. £10
Directions:	turn off A1123 between Huntingdon and St. Ives
Waters accessed:	River Great Ouse, North Sea, Middle Levels, River Nene

Town Quay, St. Ives, Cambs

Suits:	small craft only
Availability:	during daylight hours
Restrictions:	none
Facilities:	fuel nearby, parking for car and trailer(c), toilets, chandlery from The Boathaven
Licence:	EA licence
Charge:	none

Directions:	turn off eastern bypass road at the Meadow Lane junction; site is at the quay downstream of the old bridge
Waters accessed:	River Great Ouse, North Sea, Middle Levels, River Nene

The Boathaven, Low Road, St. Ives, Cambs

Tel: 01480 494040

Type:	concrete slipway
Suits:	all craft
Availability:	daily during normal working hours
Restrictions:	none
Facilities:	fuel, parking for car and trailer(c), telephone, refuse and sewage disposal, water, gas, toilets and showers, overnight moorings, chandlery, boatyard, engine repairs
Licence:	EA licence
Charge:	approx. £12
Directions:	from A14 take A1096 north to St Ives, turning right at roundabout south of St. Ives into Low Road following signs to Fenstanton, then turn off to marina
Waters accessed:	River Great Ouse, North Sea, Middle Levels, River Nene

Westview Marina, High Street, Earith, Cambs

Tel: 01487 841627

Type:	launching by crane only
Suits:	larger craft
Availability:	by prior arrangement only
Restrictions:	no slipway
Facilities:	diesel, parking for car and trailer, refuse disposal, water, gas, toilets and showers, overnight moorings, some engine repairs, caravan site
Licence:	EA licence
Charge:	approx. £15
Directions:	follow the A1123 east from Huntingdon to Earith; site is on right
Waters accessed:	River Great Ouse, North Sea, Middle Levels, River Nene

Hermitage Marina, Earith, Cambs

Tel: 01487 840994

Type:	shallow concrete slipway
Suits:	all craft up to 25'/7.6m LOA
Availability:	0830 - 1800 daily in summer, 0900 - 1600 daily in winter by prior arrangement
Restrictions:	none
Facilities:	fuel, parking for car and trailer(c), sewage and refuse disposal, pump-out, water, gas, toilets, overnight moorings, chandlery, engine repairs
Licence:	EA licence
Charge:	approx. £15
Directions:	follow the A1123 east from Huntingdon to Earith; site is on right
Waters accessed:	River Great Ouse, North Sea, Middle Levels, River Nene

Bridge Boatyard, Bridge Road, Ely, Cambs

Tel: 01353 663726

Type:	concrete slipway
Suits:	craft up to 32'/9.7m LOA
Availability:	during daylight hours
Restrictions:	steep slipway
Facilities:	parking for car and trailer(c), refuse disposal, water, gas, toilets, boatyard, tractor assistance if required, engine repairs
Licence:	EA licence
Charge:	approx. £15
Directions:	in Ely take the A142 towards Newmarket: site is near railway station
Waters accessed:	River Great Ouse, North Sea, Middle Levels, River Nene

Loveys Marine, Ely Marina, Waterside, Ely, Cambs

Te: 01353 664622 Fax: 01353 669459

Type:	shallow concrete slipway
Suits:	small powered craft and trailer-sailers up to 21'/6.4m LOA
Availability:	0900 - 1700 daily by prior arrangement
Restrictions:	none
Facilities:	fuel, parking for car and trailer(c), telephone, refuse and sewage disposal, water, gas, toilets and showers, overnight moorings, chandlery, boatyard with crane, engine repairs
Licence:	EA licence
Charge:	approx. £12 (inc. parking)
Directions:	follow the A10 from Cambridge into Ely, then follow signs to river
Waters accessed:	River Great Ouse, North Sea, Middle Levels, River Nene

Waterside, Ely, Cambs

Suits:	small craft only
Availability:	during daylight hours
Restrictions:	launching over shingle only
Facilities:	fuel, parking for car and trailer; other facilities at Ely Marina nearby
Licence:	EA licence
Charge:	none
Directions:	from A142 turn into Broad Street and follow signs to river
Waters accessed:	River Great Ouse, North Sea, Middle Levels, River Nene

Denver Sluice, Denver, Norfolk

Tel:01366 382340

Suits:	small craft
Availability:	during daylight hours
Restrictions:	tidal limit of river: obtain key from lock-keeper
Facilities:	no fuel, parking for car and trailer, pub adjacent
Licence:	EA licence
Charge:	none

Directions:	follow A10 north towards Downham Market, taking the B1507 to Denver and following signs to Sluice: site is adjacent to Jenyns Arms
Waters accessed:	River Great Ouse, North Sea, Middle Levels, River Nene

RIVER OUSE (Yorkshire) — BW (North East Region)

Waterway Manager, British Waterways, Naburn Lock, Naburn, Yorks YO1 4RU
Tel: 01904 728229

The river is tidal for 30 miles from Goole to Naburn Lock and commercial traffic still reaches York, six miles further on. It is advisable to contact the lock-keeper at Naburn the day before you wish to go through the lock Tel: 01904 728229. There is a speed limit of 5 knots in force through York from Clifton Bridge to York Motor Club premises at Fulford: elsewhere it is 6 knots.

Boroughbridge Marina, Valuation Lane, Boroughbridge, Yorks

Tel: 01423 322277 / 0585 255711

Type:	concrete slipway (1:10)
Suits:	small powered craft, canoes and rowing dinghies
Availability:	0900 - 1700 daily
Restrictions:	none
Facilities:	fuel nearby, parking for car and trailer, refuse and sewage disposal, water, toilets, showers, chandlery and boatyard
Licence:	BW licence available on site
Charge:	approx. £6
Directions:	from the A1 turn onto the B6265 to Boroughbridge signposted to marina. At T-junction in town turn left then 2nd right
Waters accessed:	Rivers Ouse and Ure, Ripon Canal, River Humber, North Sea

Linton Lock Leisureways, Lock House, Linton-on-Ouse, York

Tel: 01347 848486

Type:	concrete slipway
Suits:	small powered craft, canoes and rowing dinghies
Availability:	during working hours or by prior arrangement
Restrictions:	none
Facilities:	no fuel, parking for car and trailer, toilets, bar, restaurant, camp and caravan site
Licence:	BW licence
Charge:	approx. £5
Directions:	follow signs for RAF Linton-on-Ouse then Linton Lock Leisureways signs
Waters accessed:	Rivers Ouse and Ure, Ripon Canal, River Humber, North Sea

The Slipway, Acaster Malbis, York (Waterline Leisure)

Tel: 01904 702049 / 07885 255711

Type:	concrete slipway (1:12)
Suits:	all small craft
Availability:	during daylight hours
Restrictions:	windsurfers and pwc prohibited
Facilities:	fuel nearby, parking for car and trailer, toilets, cafe, out-

	board repairs nearby
Licence:	BW licence
Charge:	approx. £6
Directions:	turn off A64 Leeds to York road at Copmanthorpe onto A1036: turn left in Bishopthorpe, then right to Acaster Malbis
Waters accessed:	River Ure, Ripon Canal, River Humber, North Sea

York Marine Services Ltd, Ferry Lane, Bishopthorpe, North Yorks
Tel: 01904 704442/705812

Type:	steep concrete slipway
Suits:	craft up to 27'/8.2m LOA
Availability:	0830 - 1800 daily
Restrictions:	all slipping and recovery of craft is carried out by yard staff using tractor but dinghies may be launched by hand for a small charge
Facilities:	no fuel; parking for car and trailer, toilets, telephone, restaurant, moorings, boat hire, caravan site, chandlery and boatyard
Licence:	BW licence
Charge:	approx. £5
Directions:	from A64 York bypass exit on A1036 signposted to Bishopthorpe village: turn left at "T" junction in village main street, turning right into Acaster Lane for Acaster Malbis and turning left after 150m
Waters accessed:	Rivers Ouse and Ure, Ripon Canal, River Humber, North Sea

OXFORD CANAL — BW (South East Region)

Waterway Manager, British Waterways, The Stop House, Braunston, Daventry, Northants NN11 7JQ Tel: 01788 890666

One of the earliest canals in southern England, it was built to facilitate the transport of coal from the Warwickshire coalfield to Banbury and Oxford and thence the Thames. Now a very popular cruising waterway it runs for 77 miles from the junction with the Coventry Canal (Hawkesbury Junction) to Oxford where it joins the Thames. There are connections with the Grand Union Canal at Napton and Braunston Junctions. Speed limit is 4 mph.

Napton Narrowboats, Napton Marina, Napton-on-the-Hill, Stockton, Warwicks
Tel: 01926 813644

Type:	concrete slipway
Suits:	all craft
Availability:	0900 - 1730 daily by prior arrangement
Restrictions:	none
Facilities:	diesel, parking for car and trailer(c), sewage and refuse disposal, water, pump-out, toilets, overnight moorings, chandlery, boatyard
Licence:	BW licence
Charge:	yes - on application
Directions:	follow A423 north from Banbury turning onto A425 at

	Southam and following signs: site is 300 yds south of the junction of the Oxford and Grand Union canals
Waters accessed:	Oxford Canal, River Thames, Coventry Canal, Grand Union Canal

Rose Narrowboats Ltd, Fosse Way, Stretton-under-Fosse, Rugby, Warwicks

Tel: 01788 832449 Fax: 01788 832545

Suits:	craft up to 27'/8.2m LOA and 7'/2.1m wide
Availability:	during working hours by arrangement only
Restrictions:	access is restricted as slipway is on other side of canal and boats have to be transported across the canal before launching
Facilities:	fuel, parking for car and trailer(c), sewage and refuse disposal, water, gas, pump-out, overnight moorings, chandlery, boatyard
Licence:	BW licence
Charge:	yes - on application
Directions:	follow the A427 Fosse Way one mile north of Brinklow: site is by bridge 30
Waters accessed:	Oxford Canal, River Thames, Coventry Canal, Grand Union Canal

Enslow Wharf, Enslow, Kidlington, Oxfordfordshire

Tel: 01869 351321 Fax: 01869 233444 (Kingsground Narrowboats)

Type:	shallow concrete slipway
Suits:	craft up to 30'/9.4m LOA
Availability:	daily by prior arrangement
Restrictions:	site is being developed enabling craft up to 72'/21.3m LOA to be launched by 2003
Facilities:	diesel, parking for car and trailer(c), sewage and refuse disposal, gas, pump-out, toilet, showers, overnight moorings,caravan site, workshop
Licence:	BW licence
Charge:	approx. £30
Directions:	turn off A4095 next to 'Rock of Gibraltar' pub
Waters accessed:	Oxford, Coventry and Grand Union canals and River Thames

PEAK FOREST CANAL — BW (North West Region)

Waterway Manager, British Waterways, Red Bull Yard, Congleton Road South, Church Lawton, Stoke on Trent ST7 3AP Tel: 01782 785703

This canal runs from the Ashton Canal at Ashton for 14 miles to Whaley Bridge and connects with the Macclesfield Canal at Marple Junction. Speed limit is 4 mph.

New Mills Wharf, Hibbert Street, New Mills, High Peak, Derbyshire
Tel: 01663 745000

Type:	steep concrete slipway
Suits:	small powered craft, canoes and rowing dinghies
Availability:	0900 - 1700 mon - sat, 1000 - 1600 sun by prior arrangement
Restrictions:	locked gates
Facilities:	diesel, parking for car and trailer, sewage and refuse disposal, water, gas, toilets, showers, overnight moorings, chandlery and boatyard
Licence:	BW licence
Charge:	approx.£6.50
Directions:	from central Manchester follow the A6 south: at traffic lights by Swan Hotel turn down hill to New Mills taking 2nd right after railway bridge; site is at end of road
Waters accessed:	Peak Forest, Ashton and Macclesfield canals

ROCHDALE CANAL — BW (North West Region)

Waterway Manager, British Waterways, Middle Warehouse, Castle Quay, Manchester M15 4NJ Tel: 0161 819 5847

The canal was originally built as a 33 mile link over the Pennines between the Mersey and the rivers of Yorkshire. It is now navigable from Sowerby Bridge to Littleborough and connects to the Calder and Hebble at Sowerby Bridge via Tuel Lane lock. Speed limit is 4 mph.

Hebden Bridge Marina, New Road, Hebden Bridge, West Yorks
Tel: 01422 844990

Type:	medium concrete slipway
Suits:	small powered craft up to 12'/3.6m wide and 30'/9.1m LOA
Availability:	during daylight hours by prior arrangement
Restrictions:	none
Facilities:	fuel , parking for car and trailer, toilets and chandlery all nearby
Licence:	from Rochdale Canal Trust
Charge:	none
Directions:	follow A646 west from Halifax to town centre
Waters accessed:	Rochdale canal, Calder and Hebble navigation, Huddersfield Broad and Narrow canals

RIVER ROTHER — EA (Southern Region)

Environment Agency, Guildborne House, Chatsworth Road, Worthing, Sussex BN11 1LD — Tel: 01903 820692

This navigable section of the River Rother is 12 miles long and runs from Rye Harbour to Bodiam. It is hoped to re-open the connection to the Royal Military canal at Iden Lock giving a further 19 miles of cruising. Speed limit is 4 mph.

Scots Float Sluice Lock, Military Road, Rye, Sussex

Tel: 01797 223256 (office hours only)

Type:	steep concrete slipway
Suits:	small powered craft
Availability:	daily by prior arrangement only
Restrictions:	24 hour notice required, access through locked barrier
Facilities:	parking for car and trailer
Licence:	none
Charge:	none
Directions:	from Rye take A268 north then turn right towards Appledore; site is 1 mile from Rye on this road
Waters accessed:	River Rother

SELBY CANAL — BW (North East Region)

Waterway Manager, British Waterways, Naburn Lock, Naburn, Yorks YO1 4RU — Tel: 01904 728229

The Selby Canal was built in the 1770s as a link from the Aire and Calder navigation to Selby, by-passing the difficult to navigate lower reaches of the River Aire. Speed limit is 4 mph.

Selby Boat Centre, Bawtry Road, Selby

Tel: 01757 212211

Type:	shallow becoming steep concrete slipway
Suits:	all craft
Availability:	0900 - 1700 daily
Restrictions:	none
Facilities:	diesel, petrol nearby, parking for car and trailer (c if more than 1 car), toilets, water, gas, pump-out, chandlery, engine repairs, moorings
Licence:	BW licence
Charge:	approx. £7.50
Directions:	from Selby take A1041 south; site is on right
Waters accessed:	Selby Canal, Aire and Calder Canal, River Ouse

Waterway Manager, British Waterways, Llanthony Warehouse,
Gloucester Docks, Gloucester Gl1 2EH Tel: 01452 318000

One of the most important navigations in the country, linking the Midlands and Wales to the Bristol Channel and thence the open sea, a canal was built in the 19th century from Sharpness to Gloucester to improve its viability. There are connections with the River Avon at Tewkesbury, the Worcester and Birmingham Canal at Diglis Junction and the Staffs and Worcs Canal at Stourport. There is a speed limit of 6 mph above Kempsey and 8 mph below.

Lower Lode Inn, Forthampton, Tewkesbury, Glos

Tel: 01684 293224

Type:	shallow concrete slipway
Suits:	craft up to 30'/9.1m LOA except windsurfers and PWC
Availability:	during opening hours only
Restrictions:	access is via a narrow no-through lane: get permission to launch from hotel
Facilities:	no fuel, parking for car and trailer, telephone, toilets, overnight moorings, bar meals
Licence:	BW licence
Charge:	approx. £7.50
Directions:	follow A438 Tewkesbury to Ledbury road turning into Forthampton village and follow signs to Lower Lode: site is disused ferry slipway at end of road
Waters accessed:	River Severn, Bristol Channel, River Avon; Worcs and Birmingham and Staffs and Worcs canals

Upton Marina, Upton-on-Severn, Worcs

Tel: 01684 594287

Type:	steep concrete slipway
Suits:	small powered craft, canoes, sailing and rowing dinghies
Availability:	0900 - 1700 daily
Restrictions:	boats require Safety Certificate and Insurance
Facilities:	diesel, parking for car and trailer (c), telephone, sewage and refuse disposal, water, gas, pump-out, toilets and showers, overnight moorings, chandlery, boatyard, engine repairs, cafe, boat hire and sales
Licence:	BW licence
Charge:	approx. £10
Directions:	from M50 junction 1 take A38 north and then A4104 west
Waters accessed:	River Severn, Bristol Channel, River Avon; Worcs and Birmingham and Staffs and Worcs canals

Stourport Marina, Sandy Lane, Stourport, Worcs

Tel: 01299 827082

Type:	shallow concrete slipway
Suits:	small powered craft, canoes, sailing and rowing dinghies
Availability:	0900 - 1700 daily
Restrictions:	none

Facilities:	diesel, parking for car and trailer (c), telephone, sewage and refuse disposal, water, gas, pump-out, toilets and showers, overnight moorings, chandlery, engine repairs, bar, restaurant
Licence:	BW licence
Charge:	approx. £8
Directions:	from M5 junction 6 take A442 north, then A4025 to Stourport
Waters accessed:	River Severn, Bristol Channel, River Avon; Worcs and Birmingham and Staffs and Worcs canals

SHEFFIELD AND SOUTH YORKS NAVIGATION

BW (North East Region)

Waterway Manager, British Waterways, Doncaster Wharf, Greyfriars Road, Doncaster, South Yorks DN1 1QN Tel: 01302 340610

Comprising four different waterways, this navigation connects Sheffield with the sea via either the New Junction Canal, which was the last canal to be built in the country and the Aire and Calder Navigation or the Stainforth and Keadby Canal and the River Trent. Speed limit is 4 mph.

Tulleys Marine Services, The Boatyard, Northfield Road, Rotherham, South Yorks
Tel: 01709 836743

Type:	steep concrete slipway (1:7) and 18'/5.5m wide
Suits:	powered craft, canoes and rowing dinghies
Availability:	1000 - 1700 tues - fri, 1000 - 1400 sat - sun: closed mon
Restrictions:	in locked compound, contact boatyard for key
Facilities:	diesel on site, petrol nearby, parking for car and trailer, water, gas, toilets, chandlery and boatyard, 10 ton boat hoist, moorings
Licence:	BW licence
Charge:	approx. £5
Directions:	from Rotherham Inner Ring road (Centenary Way) turn north onto Greasbrough Road and take third right, then second left; site is at end of road
Waters accessed:	Sheffield and South Yorkshire Navigation, Aire and Calder Navigation, Stainforth and Keadby Canal, River Trent

SHROPSHIRE UNION CANAL

BW (North West and Midlands Regions)

Ellesmere Port to Audlem and Middlewich
Waterway Manager, British Waterways, Tower Wharf, Raymond Street, Chester CH1 3EZ Tel: 01244 390372

Audlem to Autherley
Waterway Manager, British Waterways, Norbury Junction, Norbury, Stafford ST20 OPN Tel: 01785 284253

The canal connects with the Staffordshire and Worcester Canal at Autherley Junction and the Llangollen Canal at Hurleston Junction before finally meeting the Manchester Ship Canal at Ellesmere Port. The Middlewich Branch of the canal connects the Shropshire Union to the Trent and Mersey Canal. There is a speed limit of 4 mph.

Water Travel, Autherley Junction, Oxley Moor Road, Wolverhampton
Tel: 01902 782371 Fax: 01902 787374

Type:	shallow concrete slipway
Suits:	small powered craft up to 22'/6.7m LOA, canoes and rowing dinghies
Availability:	0900 - 1700 daily by prior arrangement
Restrictions:	none
Facilities:	diesel, petrol nearby, parking for car and trailer (c), telephone, sewage and refuse disposal, water, gas, pump-out, toilets, overnight moorings, chandlery, boatyard, engine repairs
Licence:	BW licence
Charge:	approx. £15
Directions:	from Wolverhampton Ring Road take A449 north: after 2 miles approx. turn left onto Oxley Moor Road; site is on right after roundabout and canal bridge
Waters accessed:	Shropshire Union, Staffs and Worcs, Llangollen and Trent and Mersey canals

Countrywide Cruisers, The Wharf, Brewood, Staffs
Tel: 01902 850166 Fax: 01902 851662

Type:	shallow concrete slipway
Suits:	all craft
Availability:	0830 - 1700 mon - fri
Restrictions:	none
Facilities:	diesel, petrol nearby, parking for car and trailer(c), telephone, sewage and refuse disposal, water, gas, pump-out, toilet, boatyard, engine repairs
Licence:	BW licence
Charge:	approx. £15
Directions:	leave M6 at junction 12 taking A5 west: after Gailey roundabout, turn off to Brewood: turn right onto Bishops Wood Road and after canal bridge turn right by church: site is 500m down lane
Waters accessed:	Shropshire Union, Staffs and Worcs, Llangollen and Trent and Mersey canals

Anglo Welsh, The Wharf, Norbury Junction, Stafford, Staffs

Tel: 01785 284292

Type:	concrete slipway
Suits:	all craft up to 25'/7.6m LOA except ribs, PWC and windsurfers
Availability:	daily by prior arrangement
Restrictions:	access is via narrow road
Facilities:	diesel, parking for car on site, trailer nearby (c) by prior arrangement, telephone, water, gas, pump-out, toilets, overnight moorings, chandlery, boatyard, dry-dock, engine repairs, shop
Licence:	BW licence
Charge:	approx. £7.50
Directions:	leave M6 at junction 14 to Eccleshall and take A519 towards Newport. One mile after Woodseaves take second turning on the left to Norbury
Waters accessed:	Shropshire Union, Staffs and Worcs, Llangollen and Trent and Mersey canals

Holidays Afloat Ltd, The Boatyard, Newcastle Road, Market Drayton, Shropshire

Tel: 01630 652641

Type:	short concrete slipway
Suits:	powered craft up to 25'/7.6m LOA
Availability:	0930 - 1730 mon - fri: 0930 - 1330 sat;: closed sun
Restrictions:	none
Facilities:	fuel nearby, parking for car and trailer (c for more than one day), telephone, water, gas, pump-out, toilets nearby, crane, overnight moorings, chandlery: shops 10 minutes walk
Licence:	BW licence
Charge:	approx. £22
Directions:	site is off the A53 at Market Drayton
Waters accessed:	Shropshire Union, Staffs and Worcs, Llangollen and Trent and Mersey canals

Midway Boats Ltd, Barbridge Marina, Wardle, Nantwich, Cheshire

Tel: 01270 528482/528682

Type:	steep concrete slipway
Suits:	small powered craft
Availability:	0900 - 1700 daily
Restrictions:	steep slipway and narrow bridge limits width of boat to 6'10"/2.1m
Facilities:	parking for car and trailer(c), telephone, sewage and refuse disposal, water, gas, toilets, overnight moorings
Licence:	BW licence
Charge:	approx. £20
Directions:	from Nantwich follow A51 north for about 4 miles; site is on right over canal bridge
Waters accessed:	Shropshire Union, Staffs and Worcs, Llangollen and Trent and Mersey canals

BW Chester Yard, Tower Wharf, Chester, Cheshire

Tel: 01244 390372

Type:	concrete slipway
Suits:	small powered craft and rowing dinghies
Availability:	during daylight hours by prior arrangement only
Restrictions:	none
Facilities:	no fuel or parking, refuse disposal, water
Licence:	BW licence
Charge:	yes - on application
Directions:	access is from Raymond Street
Waters accessed:	Shropshire Union, Staffs and Worcs, Llangollen and Trent and Mersey canals

Middlewich Arm

Venetian Marina Village, Cholmondeston, Nantwich, Cheshire

Tel: 01270 528251

Type:	shallow concrete slipway
Suits:	small powered craft, canoes and rowing dinghies
Availability:	0900 - 1700 daily by prior arrangement
Restrictions:	craft up to 6'10"/2.1m wide only
Facilities:	diesel, parking for car and trailer, sewage and refuse disposal, water, gas, pump-out, toilets, showers, overnight moorings, chandlery, tearoom
Licence:	BW licence
Charge:	approx. £14
Directions:	leave M6 at junction 17 taking A534 to Nantwich then A51 north to Reaseheath College; 150 m after college turn right at crossroads and follow lane for 3 miles
Waters accessed:	Shropshire Union, Staffs and Worcs, Llangollen and Trent and Mersey canals

Kings Lock Boatyard, Booth Lane, Middlewich, Cheshire

Tel: 01606 737564

Type:	medium concrete slipway
Suits:	small powered craft, canoes and rowing dinghies
Availability:	0800 - 1730 mon - fri, 0900 - 1730 weekends, 0900 - 1630 Bank Holidays
Restrictions:	weight limit over canal bridge of 4½ tons, narrow road and locked barrier (max. width 9'/2.7m)
Facilities:	diesel, parking for car and trailer(c), sewage and refuse disposal, water, gas, overnight moorings, chandlery, breakdown service: toilets and petrol nearby
Licence:	BW licence
Charge:	approx. £30

Directions: leave M6 at junction 18 taking the A54 to Middlewich; at town centre traffic lights take B530 towards Sandbach for ½ mile

Waters accessed: Shropshire Union, Staffs and Worcs, Llangollen and Trent and Mersey canals

STAINFORTH AND KEADBY CANAL BW (North East Region)

Waterway Manager, British Waterways, Doncaster Wharf, Greyfriars Road, Doncaster, South Yorks DN1 1QN Tel: 01302 340610

This canal connects the Sheffield and South Yorks Navigation at Bramwith Lock with the River Trent at Keadby. Speed limit is 4 mph.

Staniland Marina, Lock Lane, Thorne, South Yorks

Tel: 01405 813150

Type:	concrete slipway
Suits:	small powered craft, canoes and rowing dinghies
Availability:	0900 - 1600 daily
Restrictions:	none
Facilities:	diesel, parking for car and trailer, refuse disposal, pump-out, water, gas, toilets, showers, telephone, overnight moorings, chandlery, pub, restaurant, boatyard with crane
Licence:	BW licence
Charge:	approx. £20
Directions:	leave M18 at junction 6 following A614 and signs to Thorne; turn into Pinfold Lane then Lock Lane
Waters accessed:	Sheffield and South Yorks Navigations, River Trent

Blue Water Marina, South End, Thorne, South Yorks

Tel: 01405 813165

Type:	shallow concrete slipway
Suits:	all craft except PWC
Availability:	by prior arrangement only
Restrictions:	none
Facilities:	diesel, petrol nearby, parking for car and trailer, sewage and refuse disposal, water, gas, pump-out, toilets and showers, overnight moorings, chandlery, boatyard, clubhouse
Licence:	BW licence
Charge:	approx. £10
Directions:	turn off M18 at junction 6: site is opposite South Station, Thorne
Waters accessed:	Sheffield and South Yorks Navigations, River Trent

STAFFORDSHIRE AND WORCESTERSHIRE CANAL

BW (Midlands Region)

Waterway Manager, British Waterways, Norbury Junction, Norbury, Stafford ST20 OPN Tel: 01785 284253

This canal joins the River Severn at Stourport and the Trent and Mersey Canal at Great Haywood Junction and runs a distance of 46 miles; there are also connections with the Birmingham Canal at Aldersley Junction and the Shropshire Union Canal at Autherley Junction. It is now a delightful canal for cruising. There is a speed limit of 4 mph.

Severn Valley Cruisers, York Street Boatyard, Stourport-on-Severn, Worcs

Tel: 01299 871165

Type:	launching by crane only
Suits:	larger craft
Availability:	during working hours by prior arrangement
Restrictions:	none
Facilities:	diesel, petrol (¼ mile), parking for car and trailer(c) nearby, sewage and refuse disposal, water, gas, pump-out, toilets, overnight moorings, chandlery and boatyard, engine repairs
Licence:	BW licence
Charge:	yes - on application
Directions:	site is off York Street: turn left immediately after crossing the canal
Waters accessed:	Staffs & Worcs, Trent and Mersey, Birmingham and Shropshire Union canals, River Severn

Teddesley Boat Company, Park Gate Lock, Teddesley Road, Penkridge, Staffs

Tel: 01785 714692

Type:	launching by crane only
Suits:	canal craft
Availability:	during working hours by arrangement
Restrictions:	launching by 32 ton crane only: no slipway
Facilities:	parking for car, sewage and refuse disposal, water, pump-out, toilets, boatyard, engine repairs
Licence:	BW licence
Charge:	yes - on application
Directions:	turn off A449 north of Penkridge: site is by bridge 90
Waters accessed:	Staffs & Worcs, Trent and Mersey, Birmingham and Shropshire Union canals, River Severn

Stafford Boat Club Ltd, Off Maplewood, Wildwood, Stafford

Tel: 01785 249806

Type:	shallow concrete slipway
Suits:	all small craft up to 6'10"/2.1m wide
Availability:	during daylight hours by prior arrangement
Restrictions:	locked gates
Facilities:	diesel, petrol nearby, short-term parking for car and trailer, toilets, clubhouse bar

Licence:	BW licence
Charge:	approx. £20
Directions:	take A34 south from Stafford town centre and turn right opposite Police HQ onto estate ring road; turn into Maplewood and down boat club private drive
Waters accessed:	Staffs & Worcs, Trent and Mersey, Birmingham and Shropshire Union canals, River Severn

STRATFORD-ON-AVON CANAL — BW (Midlands Region)

Waterway Manager, British Waterways, Brome Hall Lane, Lapworth, Solihull, West Midlands, B94 5RB — Tel: 01564 784634

Built to connect Stratford-on-Avon to the expanding canal network, it meets the Worcs and Birmingham Canal at Kings Norton, the Grand Union at Kingswood Junction and joins the River Avon in Stratford itself. There is a speed limit of 4 mph.

Lyons Boatyard, Canal Side, Limekiln Lane, Warstock, West Midlands

Tel: 0121 474 4977

Type:	launching by crane only
Suits:	larger craft
Availability:	during daylight hours by prior arrangement
Restrictions:	weight limit 10 tons
Facilities:	diesel, petrol nearby, parking for car and trailer (c), sewage disposal, water, gas, coal, pump-out, toilets and showers, overnight moorings, limited chandlery, shop, snack bar, engine repairs nearby
Licence:	BW licence
Charge:	yes - on application
Directions:	from M42 junction 3 follow A435 north: site is on right at bridge 3
Waters accessed:	Stratford-on-Avon, Worcs and Birmingham and Grand Union canals; River Avon (Warwicks)

Earlswood Motor Yacht Club, Lady Lane, Earlswood, Solihull, West Midlands

Tel: 01564 702552

Type:	concrete slipway
Suits:	small cabin cruisers only
Availability:	by prior arrangement only
Restrictions:	none
Facilities:	parking for car and trailer(c), sewage and refuse disposal, water, toilets, overnight moorings, dry dock, clubhouse
Licence:	BW licence
Charge:	yes - on application
Directions:	follow A3400 north from Stratford-on-Avon turning left onto B4102 and into Lady Lane after 2 miles
Waters accessed:	Stratford-on-Avon, Worcs and Birmingham and Grand Union canals; River Avon (Warwicks)

Swallow Cruisers, Wharf Lane, Lapworth, Solihull, West Midlands
Tel: 01564 783442

Type: medium gradient concrete slipway
Suits: small powered craft up to 30'/9.1m LOA
Availability: by prior arrangement
Restrictions: maximum width 6'10"/2.1m
Facilities: diesel, petrol nearby, parking for car and trailer, sewage and refuse disposal, water, gas, pump-out, toilets, chandlery and boatyard; shops and pub nearby
Licence: BW licence
Charge: approx. £7
Directions: from M42 junction 4 take A3400 south, turning left after canal bridge south of Hockley Heath
Waters accessed: Stratford-on-Avon, Worcs and Birmingham and Grand Union canals; River Avon (Warwickshire)

STROUDWATER CANAL

Cotswold Canals Trust, 44 Black Jack Street, Cirencester, Glos GL7 2AA
Tel: 01285 643440

Originally a short waterway built to link the River Severn with the Gloucester and Sharpness Canal and the Thames & Severn canal. Currently under restoration this section of the canal provides just over 1 mile of canal cruising. Speed limit is 4 mph.

Blunder Lock, Eastington, Gloucestershire
Tel: 01453 827414 or 01285 643440

Type: shallow concrete slipway
Suits: small powered craft, canoes and rowing dinghies
Availability: by prior arrangement only
Restrictions: locked barrier please telephone contact number for key
Facilities: fuel nearby, parking for car and trailer on site
Licence: none
Charge: approx. £5 for powered craft, £1 for non-powered
Directions: from M5 junction 13 take A419 in direction of Stroud for ½ mile; at roundabout take road signposted Eastington; site is on left after 100 m just before canal bridge
Waters accessed: Stroudwater Canal

Tees and Hartlepool Port Authority
Tel: 01642 241121

Above Tees Barrage - The River Master, Tees Barrage Ltd, Navigation Way, Thornaby, Cleveland TS18 6QA Tel: 01642 633273

A busy commercial river that has been greatly improved for pleasure boats by the construction of a tidal barrage below Stockton-on-Tees. There is now 11 miles of very pleasant non-tidal cruising above the barrage to Worsall Weir. It is a requirement that all boats using the waterway must have 3rd party insurance and be registered with Tees Barrage Ltd. There is a speed limit of 5 mph on the river and all waterborne activities are subject to the Authority's bylaws.

Tees Barrage, Navigation Way, Thornaby

Tel: 01642 633273 - VHF Ch 37 (Tees Barrage Ltd.)

Type:	shallow concrete slipway
Suits:	all craft
Availability:	at all times
Restrictions:	5 mph speed limit on river: water-skiing and pwc permitted for club members only in designated areas; all powered craft must be registered with Tees Barrage Ltd. and have proof of 3rd party liability insurance; craft intending to enter the tidal waters downstream of the lock must register with the Tees Harbour Office Tel: (01642) 277205
Facilities:	parking for car and trailer on site, boat lift up to 12 tonne @ £50
Dues:	registration fee
Charge:	approx. £10
Directions:	site is signposted off the A66 west of the A19
Waters accessed:	non-tidal River Tees or tidal river via lock and North Sea

Corporation Quay, Riverside Rd, Stockton-on-Tees

Tel: 01642 633273 - VHF Ch 37 (Tees Barrage Ltd.)

Type:	concrete slipway
Suits:	all craft up to 20'/6.1m LOA approx.
Availability:	at all times
Restrictions:	5 mph speed limit on river: water-skiing and pwc permitted for club members only in designated areas; all powered craft must be registered with Tees Barrage Ltd. and have proof of 3rd party liability insurance; all users must sign a disclaimer from Stockton B.C.; craft intending to enter the tidal waters downstream of the lock must register with the Tees Harbour Office Tel: (01642) 277205
Facilities:	petrol nearby, parking for car and trailer
Dues:	registration fee
Charge:	none
Directions:	follow A1(M) north turning off onto A66 and following signs to Stockton: access is via car park in Riverside Road
Waters accessed:	non-tidal River Tees, tidal river (via lock) and North Sea

RIVER THAMES

NON-TIDAL: CRICKLADE TO TEDDINGTON

EA (Thames Region)

Kings Meadow House, Kings Meadow Road, Reading, Berks RG1 8DQ
Tel: 01189 535000

The river runs for 215 miles from its source beyond Cricklade to the Thames Estuary. By the end of the 19th century it was linked to the main canal network giving access to many other parts of the country. All boats using the non-tidal river must be registered with and licensed by the EA. The speed limit is 8 knots.

Riverside Lechlade, Parkend Wharf, Lechlade, Glos

Tel: 07712 418111

Type:	concrete slipway
Suits:	small craft
Availability:	during daylight hours by prior arrangement
Restrictions:	none
Facilities:	fuel, parking for car and trailer(c), telephone, water, gas, toilet, showers, overnight moorings, chandlery, boatyard, engine repairs, pub
Licence:	EA licence
Charge:	approx. £7
Directions:	follow A361 to Lechlade town centre turning down to Riverside
Waters accessed:	Rivers Thames and Wey, Oxford, Kennet and Avon and Grand Union canals

Ferryman Inn, Bablock Hythe, Oxon

Tel: 01865 880028

Type:	steep concrete slipway on west bank
Suits:	small craft
Availability:	during daylight hours by prior arrangement
Restrictions:	none
Facilities:	pub, caravan site nearby, parking
Licence:	EA licence
Charge:	approx. £10
Directions:	from Eynsham bypass take B4449 to Stanton Harcourt turning left for village centre then through West End to river
Waters accessed:	Rivers Thames and Wey, Oxford, Kennet and Avon and Grand Union canals

Bablock Hythe, Oxon

Type:	steep concrete slipway on east bank
Suits:	small craft
Availability:	during daylight hours
Restrictions:	none
Facilities:	none

Licence:	EA licence
Charge:	none
Directions:	turn off B4017 by Post Office in Cumnor in village centre follow road to river
Waters accessed:	Rivers Thames and Wey, Oxford, Kennet and Avon and Grand Union canals

Oxford Cruisers, The Boat Hire Centre, Eynsham, Witney, Oxon

Tel: 01865 881698

Type:	shallow concrete slipway
Suits:	all trailable craft except pwc
Availability:	0800 - 1800 daily by prior arrangement only
Restrictions:	Swinford toll bridge is fairly narrow: drivers towing large craft may need to find an alternative route; locked barrier out of working hours
Facilities:	fuel, parking for car and trailer(c), telephone, refuse and sewage disposal, water, gas, pump-out, toilets and showers, overnight moorings, boatyard with 5 ton boat lift, engine repairs, shop
Licence:	EA licence
Charge:	approx. £7.50
Directions:	from Oxford ring road take the A40 towards Cheltenham turning left at Jet station roundabout for Eynsham: go through town and over Swinford toll bridge (5p charge) on B4044 turning right after ½ mile opposite Stroud Copse
Waters accessed:	Rivers Thames and Wey, Oxford, Kennet and Avon and Grand Union canals

Bossoms Boatyard Ltd, Medley, Binsey Lane, Oxford, Oxon

Tel: 01865 247780

Type:	shallow concrete slipway
Suits:	all craft except ribs, PWC and windsurfers
Availability:	0900 - 1700 mon - fri and 0900 - noon sat by prior arrangement
Restrictions:	closed sat pm and sun, narrow access road
Facilities:	no fuel, parking for car and trailer, telephone, water, toilets, overnight moorings, chandlery and boatyard with 4 ton gantry
Licence:	EA licence
Charge:	approx. £17.40
Directions:	from ring road, take A420 Botley Road into Oxford turning left into Binsey Lane to village and then right to yard
Waters accessed:	Rivers Thames and Wey, Oxford, Kennet and Avon and Grand Union canals

Osney Marina, Mill Street, Botley, Oxford, Oxon

Tel: 01865 241348

Type:	concrete slipway
Suits:	all craft
Availability:	during daylight hours by prior arrangement
Restrictions:	none

Facilities: diesel, parking on site for car and trailer, water, refuse and sewage disposal, pump-out, toilets, moorings, engine repairs
Licence: EA licence
Charge: approx. £10 includes one day parking for car & trailer
Directions: from ring road, take A420 Botley Road into Oxford turning right into Mill Lane after bridge over river
Waters accessed: Rivers Thames and Wey, Oxford, Kennet and Avon and Grand Union canals

Riverside Centre, Donnington Bridge, via Meadow Lane, Oxford, Oxon

Tel: 01865 248673

Type: shallow concrete slipway
Suits: small craft
Availability: during daylight hours
Restrictions: controlled by key available from centre in advance
Facilities: limited parking on site, boatyard nearby
Licence: EA licence
Charge: approx. £5
Directions: from Oxford ring road take A423 east at South Hinksey interchange, turn left after crossing railway line onto B4144 and then right over bridge; site is upstream of bridge on east bank
Waters accessed: Rivers Thames and Wey, Oxford, Kennet and Avon and Grand Union canals

Abingdon Boat Centre, The Bridge, Nags Head Island, Abingdon, Oxon

Tel: 01235 521125 Fax:01235 535515

Type: steep concrete slipway and slip plates
Suits: small craft up to 21'/6.4m LOA except pwc
Availability: during working hours only by prior arrangement
Restrictions: narrow entrance from road; vehicle ramp down to car park and slip
Facilities: diesel, parking for car and trailer(c) by prior arrangement, water, gas, pump-out, chandlery; petrol and toilets nearby
Licence: EA licence
Charge: approx. £5
Directions: follow A415 to Abingdon town centre: site is by bridge and opposite the Mill House Inn
Waters accessed: Rivers Thames and Wey, Oxford, Kennet and Avon and Grand Union canals

St. Helen's Wharf, East Street, Abingdon, Oxon

Type: steep and narrow cobbled ramp
Suits: very small craft only
Availability: during daylight hours
Restrictions: access is via narrow one-way street
Facilities: pub opposite, limited parking nearby
Licence: EA licence
Charge: none

Directions:	follow A415 to Abingdon town centre, turning off High Street into West St Helen's Street or East St Helen's Street to the river: site is near St.Helen's church and opposite the Old Anchor Pub
Waters accessed:	Rivers Thames and Wey, Oxford, Kennet and Avon and Grand Union canals

The Lees, Clifton Hampden, Oxon

Tel: 01865 407828

Type:	concrete slipway
Suits:	small to medium craft only
Availability:	during daylight hours by prior arrangement
Restrictions:	none
Facilities:	no fuel, parking for car and trailer(c), pub nearby
Licence:	EA licence
Charge:	yes - on application
Directions:	follow A415 into Clifton Hampden turning off into village and taking road across the bridge: site is on east bank of river upstream of the bridge and near the Barley Mow Inn
Waters accessed:	Rivers Thames and Wey, Oxford, Kennet and Avon and Grand Union canals

Benson Waterfront, Benson, Oxon

Tel: 01491 838304

Type:	medium concrete slipway
Suits:	small powered craft, canoes, sailing and rowing dinghies
Availability:	0830 - 1730 daily
Restrictions:	none
Facilities:	diesel, petrol nearby, parking for car and trailer(c), telephone, sewage and refuse disposal, water, gas, pump-out, toilets and showers, overnight moorings, launderette, restaurant, shop
Licence:	EA licence
Charge:	approx. £10
Directions:	site is on A423 Henley to Oxford road near the junction with the B4009, just upriver of Benson Lock on the east bank
Waters accessed:	Rivers Thames and Wey, Oxford, Kennet and Avon and Grand Union canals

Papist Way, Cholsey, Nr. Wallingford, Oxon

Type:	hard shingle
Suits:	small craft only
Availability:	during daylight hours
Restrictions:	none
Facilities:	parking, pub nearby
Licence:	EA licence
Charge:	none
Directions:	turn off A329 south of Wallingford by Fair Mile Hospital
Waters accessed:	Rivers Thames and Wey, Oxford, Kennet and Avon and Grand Union canals

Sheridan Uk Marine, Moulsford, Oxon

Tel: 01491 652085

Type:	concrete slipway
Suits:	all craft
Availability:	during working hours by prior arrangement: closed winter week-ends
Restrictions:	assisted launch only: access limited by small bridge
Facilities:	diesel, parking for car and trailer(c), water, gas, chandlery, boatyard
Charge:	yes - on application
Directions:	site is off A329 south of Wallingford on the west bank and just downstream of Moulsford Railway Bridge
Waters accessed:	Rivers Thames and Wey, Oxford, Kennet and Avon and Grand Union canals

Beetle and Wedge Hotel, Moulsford, Oxon

Tel: 01491 651381

Type:	shallow concrete slipway
Suits:	small craft only
Availability:	during daylight hours by prior arrangement only
Restrictions:	none
Facilities:	hotel adjacent offers food and accommodation, overnight moorings
Licence:	EA licence
Charge:	none
Directions:	follow A329 south from Wallingford, turning down to the river in Moulsford: site is at old ferry crossing beside the hotel
Waters accessed:	Rivers Thames and Wey, Oxford, Kennet and Avon and Grand Union canals

Caversham Bridge, Reading, Berks

Type:	concrete slipway
Suits:	small craft
Availability:	during daylight hours
Restrictions:	none
Facilities:	available locally
Licence:	EA licence
Charge:	none
Directions:	follow A4155: site is immediately upstream of bridge on south bank
Waters accessed:	Rivers Thames and Wey, Oxford, Kennet and Avon and Grand Union canals

Ferry Lane, Off Church Street, Wargrave, Berks

Suits:	very small craft
Availability:	during daylight hours
Restrictions:	not suitable for towed trailers
Facilities:	in village: pub nearby

Licence:	EA licence
Charge:	none
Directions:	turn into Ferry Lane from the High Street by the Greyhound pub
Waters accessed:	Rivers Thames and Wey, Oxford, Kennet and Avon and Grand Union canals

Val Wyatt Marine, Willow Marina, Willow Lane, Wargrave, Berkshire

Tel: 0118 940 3211

Type:	concrete slipway
Suits:	all craft
Availability:	during working hours by prior arrangement
Restrictions:	none
Facilities:	parking for car and trailer(c), water, refuse and sewage disposal, pump-out, gas, telephone, chandlery, boatyard, toilets
Charge:	approx. £20
Directions:	from Wargrave follow theA321 towards Henley, turning left into Willow Lane
Waters accessed:	Rivers Thames and Wey, Oxford, Kennet and Avon and Grand Union canals

Hobbs and Sons Ltd, Wargrave Road, Henley-on-Thames, Oxon

Tel: 01491 572035

Type:	shallow concrete slipway
Suits:	craft up to 25'/7.6m LOA 8'/2.4m beam and 1'6"/0.5m draught
Availability:	0830 - 1730 daily: closed weekends nov - mar
Restrictions:	none
Facilities:	parking for car and trailer(c), water; fuel, chandlery and toilets nearby
Licence:	EA licence
Charge:	approx. £10 plus £20 key deposit
Directions:	from M4/M40 via A404 and A4130: site is ½ mile outside Henley on the A321 Henley to Wargrave road
Waters accessed:	Rivers Thames and Wey, Oxford, Kennet and Avon and Grand Union canals

Wharf Lane, Henley-on-Thames, Oxon

Type:	shallow concrete slipway
Suits:	small craft
Availability:	during daylight hours
Restrictions:	locked barrier: keys from Town Hall (Tel: 01491 578034)
Facilities:	available locally
Licence:	EA licence
Charge:	none
Directions:	cross over Henley Bridge on A432 and turn right at Red Lion Hotel: launch at end of Wharf Lane, downstream of the bridge on the west bank
Waters accessed:	Rivers Thames and Wey, Oxford, Kennet and Avon and Grand Union canals

Aston Ferry, Hambleden, Bucks

Type:	shingle hard
Suits:	small craft
Availability:	during daylight hours; launch from either bank at disused ferry slipways
Restrictions:	none
Facilities:	South bank, room to park alongside track, Flower Pot Hotel nearby
Licence:	EA licence
Charge:	none
Directions:	from Henley; follow A4130 turning left on Remenham Hill to Aston for south bank or A4155 towards Marlow turning right at Mill End for north bank
Waters accessed:	Rivers Thames and Wey, Oxford, Kennet and Avon and Grand Union canals

Medmenham, Bucks

Type:	shingle hard
Suits:	small craft
Availability:	during daylight hours
Restrictions:	soft bottom
Facilities:	EA licence
Charge:	none
Directions:	turn off A4155 in Medmenham opposite the Dog and Badger Inn
Waters accessed:	Rivers Thames and Wey, Oxford, Kennet and Avon and Grand Union canals

Hurley Farm, Riverside Picnic Grounds, Hurley, Berks

Tel: 01628 823501

Type:	shallow concrete slipway
Suits:	small craft up to 20'/6.1m LOA
Availability:	0800 to dusk daily, Easter - end Sept
Restrictions:	locked access after opening hours
Facilities:	parking for car and trailer(c if overnight), toilets, telephone camping and caravans on site: fuel, chandlery and boatyard from Peter Freebody and Co, Mill Lane, Hurley
Licence:	EA licence
Charge:	approx. £4 mon - sat; £10 sun
Directions:	leave M4 at junction 8/9 taking A404 (M): at 3rd exit take A4130 towards Henley-on-Thames; after 2¾ miles turn right into Shepherds Lane and follow signs
Waters accessed:	Rivers Thames and Wey, Oxford, Kennet and Avon and Grand Union canals

Marlow Marine, Harleyford Marina, Henley Road, Marlow, Bucks

Tel: 01628 471361

Type:	small concrete slipway
Suits:	craft up to max 20'/6.1m LOA

Availability:	by prior arrangement only
Restrictions:	difficult site - please call for advice
Facilities:	diesel, sewage and refuse disposal, gas, toilets and showers, telephone, overnight moorings, chandlery, engine repairs, bar/restaurant
Licence:	EA licence
Charge:	yes - on application
Directions:	leave M4 at junction 4 taking A404 and A4155 through Marlow: site is on north bank
Waters accessed:	Rivers Thames and Wey, Oxford, Kennet and Avon and Grand Union canals

St. Peter's Street, Marlow, Bucks

Type:	shallow concrete slipway
Suits:	canoes, dinghies and small craft
Availability:	during daylight hours
Restrictions:	slipway forms end of road, no room to turn or park
Facilities:	from Harleyford Marina
Licence:	EA licence
Charge:	none
Directions:	turn off A4155 into High Street in Marlow: turn left at end of street into Station Road, then right into St. Peter's Street
Waters accessed:	Rivers Thames and Wey, Oxford, Kennet and Avon and Grand Union canals

Ferry Inn, Cookham, Berks

Type:	medium concrete and shingle hard
Suits:	small craft
Availability:	during daylight hours
Restrictions:	none
Facilities:	fuel, parking for car and trailer, telephone, toilets, pub
Charge:	none
Directions:	from Marlow follow A4094 to Cookham turning into Odney Lane opposite the High Street and then turning left immediately; site is immediately downstream of Harvester Ferry Inn
Waters accessed:	Rivers Thames and Wey, Oxford, Kennet and Avon and Grand Union canals

Ferry Road, Bray, Berks

Type:	shingle hard
Suits:	very small craft
Availability:	during daylight hours
Restrictions:	next to Waterside Inn access difficult because of restaurant traffic
Facilities:	none
Licence:	EA licence
Charge:	none

Directions: turn off B3028 into Ferry Road: launch from disused ferry slipway adjacent to Waterside Inn
Waters accessed: Rivers Thames and Wey, Oxford, Kennet and Avon and Grand Union canals

Windsor Marina, Maidenhead Road, Windsor, Berks

Tel: 01753 853911 Fax: 01753 868195

Type: shallow concrete slipway onto shingle
Suits: craft up to 20'/6.1m LOA
Availability: during daylight hours
Restrictions: none
Facilities: fuel, parking for car and trailer, sewage and refuse disposal, water, gas, pump-out, toilets and showers, telephone, moorings, chandlery and boatyard with crane; engine repairs nearby
Licence: EA licence
Charge: approx. £12.50 inc. parking
Directions: leave M4 at junction 9 taking A308 towards Windsor
Waters accessed: Rivers Thames and Wey, Oxford, Kennet and Avon and Grand Union canals

Windsor Leisure Centre, Clewer Mead, Stovell Road, Windsor, Berks

Tel: 01753 850004

Type: concrete slipway
Suits: small powered craft up to 22'/6.7m LOA, canoes and rowing dinghies
Availability: during daylight hours
Restrictions: locked barrier
Facilities: parking for car and trailer (c), water, toilets, telephone, refuse disposal, moorings; fuel etc. from Windsor Marina
Licence: EA licence
Charge: approx. £5; purchase token from Reception
Directions: leave M4 at junction 6 taking A332 towards Windsor; after dual carriageway and Thames crossing the centre is visible on left in Stovell Road
Waters accessed: Rivers Thames and Wey, Oxford, Kennet and Avon and Grand Union canals

Truss's Island, Chertsey Lane, Staines, Middlesex

Type: shallow concrete slip
Suits: small craft
Availability: during daylight hours
Restrictions: max. trailer width approx.8'/2.4m; access height restriction approx. 9'/2.7m
Facilities: parking for car & trailer, fuel from garage nearby, picnic site
Licence: EA licence
Charge: none

Directions:	from Staines take A320 towards Chertsey; site is on left on Surrey bank and access is through car park
Waters accessed:	Rivers Thames and Wey, Oxford, Kennet and Avon and Grand Union canals

Penton Hook Marina, Staines Road, Chertsey, Surrey

Tel: 01932 568681

Type:	steep concrete slipway
Suits:	craft up to 20'/6.1m LOA
Availability:	0800 - 1900 daily
Restrictions:	none
Facilities:	fuel, parking for car and trailer(c), telephone, sewage and refuse disposal, water, gas, pump-out, toilets and showers, moorings, chandlery and boatyard with crane, engine repairs
Licence:	EA licence
Charge:	approx. £10
Directions:	follow signs on A320 to Thorpe Park and marina is opposite
Waters accessed:	Rivers Thames and Wey, Oxford, Kennet and Avon and Grand Union canals

Laleham, Surrey

Type:	shallow concrete slipway
Suits:	small craft
Availability:	during daylight hours
Restrictions:	none
Facilities:	none
Licence:	EA licence
Charge:	none
Directions:	take B376 Shepperton Road from Staines towards Laleham turning down to river by Three Horseshoes pub
Waters accessed:	Rivers Thames and Wey, Oxford, Kennet and Avon and Grand Union canals

Chertsey Meads Marine, Mead Lane, Chertsey, Surrey

Tel: 01932 564699

Type:	concrete slipway
Suits:	craft up to 21'/6.4m LOA except PWC and windsurfers
Availability:	0900 - 1800 daily
Restrictions:	by prior arrangement at peak times eg. sat am; single track road: height barrier
Facilities:	diesel on site, petrol nearby, parking for car and trailer(c), refuse disposal, water, gas, limited chandlery, boatyard, moorings
Licence:	EA licence
Charge:	yes - on application

Directions:	from M25 junction 11 take A317 towards Chertsey, following dual carriageway to roundabout and taking first exit; carry on over traffic lights taking Mead Lane, (3rd road on right); follow for ½ mile taking first private road on left and follow to end
Waters accessed:	Rivers Thames and Wey, Oxford, Kennet and Avon and Grand Union canals

Thames Street, Weybridge, Surrey

Type:	shallow concrete slipway
Suits:	small craft
Availability:	during daylight hours
Restrictions:	none
Facilities:	available locally
Charge:	none
Directions:	turn off M25 at junction 11 taking A317 to Weybridge: site is adjacent to Weybridge Marine at the junction of Walton Lane and Thames Street
Waters accessed:	Rivers Thames and Wey, Oxford, Kennet and Avon and Grand Union canals

Nauticalia Boats, Ferry Lane, Shepperton, Middlesex

Tel: 01932 254844

Type:	shallow concrete slipway
Suits:	craft up to 42'/12.8m LOA
Availability:	during working hours by prior arrangement
Restrictions:	pwc prohibited
Facilities:	fuel nearby, parking for car and trailer(c), water, toilets, chandlery, shop and boatyard
Licence:	EA licence
Charge:	approx. £20
Directions:	from M25 junction 11 take A317 towards Chertsey, following dual carriageway to roundabout and taking first exit; carry on over traffic lights then turn right at next traffic lights onto B375.; follow road and take right to village centre, Ferry Lane is right turn in village
Waters accessed:	Rivers Thames and Wey, Oxford, Kennet and Avon and Grand Union canals

Shepperton Village Wharf, Shepperton, Middlesex

Type:	shallow concrete slipway
Suits:	small craft
Availability:	during daylight hours
Restrictions:	water may be very shallow in summer and Shepperton village can be very congested
Facilities:	limited parking for car & trailer, other facilities available locally
Licence:	EA licence
Charge:	none

Directions:	follow B375 to Shepperton church: site is at end of road by Anchor Hotel
Waters accessed:	Rivers Thames and Wey, Oxford, Kennet and Avon and Grand Union canals

Gibbs Marine Sales, Sandhills, Russell Road, Shepperton, Middlesex

Tel: 01932 242977

Type:	steep concrete slipway with metal fascia
Suits:	craft up to 25'/7.6m LOA
Availability:	0900 - 1800 mon - sat; 1000 - 1600 sun by prior arrangement
Restrictions:	pwc prohibited unless with liicence
Facilities:	fuel nearby, parking for car and trailer, toilets, crane, engine repairs
Licence:	EA licence
Charge:	approx. £12
Directions:	leave the M25 at junction 11 taking the A317 to Chertsey then follow B375 to Shepperton: site is in Russell road opposite the Ship Hotel
Waters accessed:	Rivers Thames and Wey, Oxford, Kennet and Avon and Grand Union canals

Bridge Marine, Thames Meadow, Shepperton, Middlesex

Tel: 01932 245126

Type:	shallow concrete slipway
Suits:	craft up to 24'/7.3m LOA on appropriate trailer
Availability:	1000 - 1700 daily: closed over Christmas
Restrictions:	only 6 DIY launches per day permitted: check for availability
Facilities:	petrol nearby, parking for car only, toilets, overnight moorings, chandlery and boatyard with 10 ton boat hoist
Licence:	EA licence
Charge:	none
Directions:	leave M25 at junction 11 taking the A317 and A244 across the bridge and turn left and left again into Walton Lane and then into Thames Meadow
Waters accessed:	Rivers Thames and Wey, Oxford, Kennet and Avon and Grand Union canals

Shepperton Marina, Felix Lane, Shepperton, Middlesex

Tel: 01932 247427

Type:	launching by crane only
Suits:	larger craft up to 35 tons
Availability:	by prior arrangement
Restrictions:	no slipway: suitable for larger craft only
Facilities:	fuel, parking for car and trailer, refuse and sewage disposal, pump-out, water, gas, toilets and showers, chandlery and boatyard
Licence:	EA licence
Charge:	yes - on application

Directions: turn off M25 at junction 11 taking A317 then A3050 to Walton-on-Thames; turn left onto A244 over bridge; at roundabout turn right and follow signs to 'Moat House': site is downstream of bridge on north bank

Waters accessed: Rivers Thames and Wey, Oxford, Kennet and Avon and Grand Union canals

Cowey Sale, Walton-on-Thames, Surrey

Type: concrete slipway

Suits: small craft

Availability: during daylight hours

Restrictions: barrier limits height on entrance to car park

Facilities: parking for car and trailer, other facilities available locally

Licence: EA licence

Charge: none

Directions: turn off M25 at junction 11 taking A317 then A3050 to Walton-on-Thames; turn left onto A244 then left just before bridge: site is on south bank upriver of Walton Bridge

Waters accessed: Rivers Thames and Wey, Oxford, Kennet and Avon and Grand Union canals

Walton Wharf, By Anglers Hotel, Walton-on-Thames, Surrey

Type: stone ramp

Suits: small craft

Availability: during daylight hours

Restrictions: drop at end of slipway; parking can be difficult and area congested

Facilities: available locally: pub adjacent

Licence: EA licence

Charge: none

Directions: site is adjacent to Anglers Hotel in Manor Road, Walton-on-Thames

Waters accessed: Rivers Thames and Wey, Oxford, Kennet and Avon and Grand Union canals

Lower Hampton Road, Sunbury, Surrey

Type: shallow concrete slipway

Suits: small craft

Availability: during working hours

Restrictions: none

Facilities: available locally

Licence: EA licence

Charge: none

Directions: follow B375 west from Hampton: site is just upriver of Sunbury Court opposite Sunbury Court Island

Waters accessed: Rivers Thames and Wey, Oxford, Kennet and Avon and Grand Union canals

Hurst Park, West Molesey, Surrey

Type: shallow concrete slipway
Suits: small craft
Availability: during daylight hours
Restrictions: slip can be blocked by large swan and duck population!
Facilities: parking for car and trailer, other facilities available locally
Licence: EA licence
Charge: none
Directions: follow Hurst Road (A3050) west from Hampton Court Bridge turning off into Sadlers Ride: site is opposite Garrick's Ait
Waters accessed: Rivers Thames and Wey, Oxford, Kennet and Avon and Grand Union canals

Thames Ditton, Surrey

Type: concrete slipway
Suits: small craft
Availability: during daylight hours
Restrictions: often blocked by parked vehicles
Facilities: available locally: pub adjacent
Licence: EA licence
Charge: none
Directions: turn off A309 into Summer Road: site is next to Swan Hotel and opposite Thames Ditton Island
Waters accessed: Rivers Thames and Wey, Oxford, Kennet and Avon and Grand Union canals

Ditton Reach, Thames Ditton, Surrey

Type: shallow concrete slipway
Suits: small craft
Availability: during daylight hours
Restrictions: in corner of housing development, access restricted, parking difficult
Facilities: available locally
Licence: EA licence
Charge: none
Directions: turn off A307 into Ditton Reach
Waters accessed: Rivers Thames and Wey, Oxford, Kennet and Avon and Grand Union canals

By Canbury Gardens, Lower Ham Road, Kingston-upon-Thames, Surrey

Tel: 020 8547 5500 (Royal Borough of Kingston)

Type: shallow concrete slipway
Suits: small craft
Availability: during daylight hours
Restrictions: none
Facilities: available locally
Licence: EA licence
Charge: none

Directions:	follow A308 to Kingston Bridge: launch from east bank downriver of bridge and adjacent to Turks Boatyard
Waters accessed:	Rivers Thames and Wey, Oxford, Kennet and Avon and Grand Union canals

BELOW TEDDINGTON LOCK (Tidal River)

Port of London Authority

Devon House, 58 - 60 St Katherine's Way, London E1 9LB
Tel: 020 7265 2656 Fax: 020 7265 2699

Pleasure craft should keep clear of commercial vessels and beware strong currents which may carry them into moored barges. Speed should be limited to prevent excess wash: above Wandsworth Bridge there is a speed limit of 8 knots. It is strongly recommended that before launching at any of the sites listed below, visitors should contact the Harbour Master (see below) for the latest information regarding navigation on the river and availability of sites which may sometimes be obstructed by commercial craft.

Upper Section (Twickenham - Dagenham) 020 8855 0315

Teddington Draw Dock, Ferry Road, Teddington, Middx.
Tel: 020 8977 9978 (The Boat Shop)

Type	shallow concrete slipway
Suits:	craft up to 15'/4.6m LOA
Availability:	launching into 6'/1.8m water at HWS: 2'/0.6 drop at end of slipway at LW
Restrictions:	get key to locked gate from The Boat Shop adjacent
Facilities:	fuel (2 miles), limited parking for car only, refuse disposal and water at lock, chandlery from The Boat Shop
Licence:	none
Charge:	none
Directions:	from Kingston Bridge follow A310 towards Twickenham turning right into Ferry Road at traffic lights by church; site is at end of road just downriver of lock
Waters accessed:	Rivers Thames and Wey, Grand Union and Oxford canals, North Sea

Church Lane, Twickenham, Middx

Type:	hard gravel foreshore
Suits:	small craft only
Availability:	tidal site: no launching at LW
Restrictions:	narrow access
Facilities:	available locally, pub nearby
Licence:	none
Charge:	none
Directions:	turn off A305 in Twickenham into Church Street and then into Church Lane and follow to Embankment
Waters accessed:	Rivers Thames and Wey, Grand Union and Oxford canals, North Sea

Riverside, Twickenham, Middx

Suits:	small craft only
Availability:	tidal site: no launching at LW
Restrictions:	narrow access
Facilities:	fuel available locally, pub nearby
Licence:	none
Charge:	none
Directions:	follow the A305 into Twickenham, turn into Sion Road & follow to Riverside: site is opposite White Swan Inn
Waters accessed:	Rivers Thames and Wey, Grand Union and Oxford canals, North Sea

Ham Landing, Ham, Surrey

Type:	gravel hard
Suits:	small craft
Availability:	tidal site: no launching at LW
Restrictions:	popular site which can be congested
Facilities:	parking in adjacent car park
Licence:	none
Charge:	none
Directions:	from Kingston follow A307 towards Richmond, turning left into Dukes Avenue or Ham Street & follow to Ham Landing
Waters accessed:	Rivers Thames and Wey, Grand Union and Oxford canals, North Sea

River Lane, Petersham, Surrey

Type:	hard gravel foreshore
Suits:	small craft
Availability:	tidal site: best launching near HW
Restrictions:	site may be congested
Facilities:	none
Charge:	none
Directions:	from Richmond on Thames follow A307 towards Kingston, turning right on sharp bend into River Lane
Waters accessed:	Rivers Thames and Wey, Grand Union and Oxford canals, North Sea

Drawdock, Water Lane, Richmond, Surrey

Type:	concrete slipway
Suits:	small craft
Availability:	tidal site: best launching near HW
Restrictions:	site is often congested and access is very narrow
Facilities:	available locally
Licence:	none
Charge:	none
Directions:	follow A307/A305 to Richmond centre and turn into Water Lane; site is just downriver of Richmond Bridge
Waters accessed:	Rivers Thames and Wey, Grand Union and Oxford canals, North Sea

London Apprentice Inn, Church Street, Isleworth, London

Type:	shallow concrete slipway
Suits:	craft up to 40'/12m LOA and 10'/3m wide
Availability:	tidal site: best launching for approximately 2 hours either side of HW
Restrictions:	none
Facilities:	fuel, parking for car and trailer, toilets, telephone
Licence:	none
Charge:	none
Directions:	turn off A315 onto A310 (Twickenham Rd) then left into Park Road and Church Street
Waters accessed:	Rivers Thames and Wey, Grand Union and Oxford canals, North Sea

Kew Bridge Drawdock, Kew, London

Suits:	small craft
Availability:	tidal site: launch near HW
Restrictions:	site is very muddy at LW
Facilities:	none
Licence:	none
Charge:	none
Directions:	site is adjacent to and downstream of bridge on north bank of river
Waters accessed:	Rivers Thames and Wey, Grand Union and Oxford canals, North Sea

Grove Park Drawdock, Kew, London

Suits:	small craft
Availability:	tidal site: launch near HW
Restrictions:	congested access
Facilities:	none
Licence:	none
Charge:	none
Directions:	from A4 at Chiswick take A316 towards Richmond; at Dukes Meadows turn right into Hartington Road and follow to Grove Park Road; site is at end of road immediately downriver of Kew railway bridge
Waters accessed:	Rivers Thames and Wey, Grand Union and Oxford canals, North Sea

Ship Drawdock, Mortlake, London

Suits:	small craft
Availability:	tidal site: launch near HW
Restrictions:	park well above tidal limit, road may flood at HW
Facilities:	parking close by, pub
Licence:	none
Charge:	none

Directions: from Richmond follow A316 then A3003 towards Mortlake; turning left into Ship Lane
Waters accessed: Rivers Thames and Wey, Grand Union and Oxford canals, North Sea

Small Profits Drawdock, Barnes, London

Suits: small craft
Availability: best launching near HW
Restrictions: access may be congested
Facilities: none
Licence: none
Charge: none
Directions: from Richmond follow A316 then A3003 to Barnes, turning left into Lonsdale Road; site is turning off Lonsdale Road
Waters accessed: Rivers Thames and Wey, Grand Union and Oxford canals, North Sea

Chiswick Church Drawdock, Church Street, Chiswick, London

Type: concrete slipway
Suits: small craft
Availability: tidal site: launch near HW
Restrictions: access may be congested
Facilities: none
Licence: none
Charge: none
Directions: from A4 at Chiswick turn into Church Street off Hogarth roundabout; site is at end of road
Waters accessed: Rivers Thames and Wey, Grand Union and Oxford canals, North Sea

Hammersmith Drawdock, Hammersmith, London

Suits: small craft
Availability: tidal site: launch near HW
Restrictions: access may be congested
Facilities: none
Licence: none
Charge: none
Directions: site is downriver of Hammersmith Bridge
Waters accessed: Rivers Thames and Wey, Grand Union and Oxford canals, North Sea

Putney Draw Dock, Putney, London

Type: concrete slipway
Suits: small craft
Availability: tidal site: best launching near HW
Restrictions: access may be congested
Facilities: none
Licence: none
Charge: none

Directions:	from Putney High Street turn left before bridge into Richmond Road then right onto the Embankment; site is immediately upriver of Putney Bridge
Waters accessed:	Rivers Thames and Wey, Grand Union and Oxford canals, North Sea

Brewhouse Street, Putney, London

Suits:	small craft
Availability:	tidal site: launch near HW
Restrictions:	access may be congested
Facilities:	none
Licence:	none
Charge:	yes - on application
Directions:	from Putney High Street turn into Putney Bridge Road then left into Brewhouse Street
Waters accessed:	Rivers Thames and Wey, Grand Union and Oxford canals, North Sea

Battersea Drawdock, Battersea, London

Suits:	small craft
Availability:	tidal site: launch near HW
Restrictions:	access may be congested
Facilities:	none
Licence:	none
Charge:	none
Directions:	site is near Church and access is from Battersea Church Road, a turning off Battersea Bridge Road
Waters accessed:	Rivers Thames and Wey, Grand Union and Oxford canals, North Sea

Newcastle Drawdock and Johnsons Drawdock, Isle of Dogs, London

Type:	concrete slipway
Suits:	small craft
Availability:	tidal site: launch near HW
Restrictions:	site may be congested
Facilities:	none
Licence:	none
Charge:	none
Directions:	access is from Saunders Ness Road off Manchester Road
Waters accessed:	Rivers Thames and Wey, Grand Union and Oxford canals, North Sea

Samuda Housing Estate, Isle of Dogs, London

Type:	concrete slipway
Suits:	small craft
Availability:	tidal site: launch within 3 hours HW
Restrictions:	none
Facilities:	parking for car and trailer nearby
Licence:	none

Charge: none
Directions: access is from Manchester Road
Waters accessed: Rivers Thames and Wey, Grand Union and Oxford canals, North Sea

Point Drawdock, Greenwich, London

Suits: small craft
Availability: tidal site: launch near HW
Restrictions: access may be congested
Facilities: none
Charge: none
Directions: from Greenwich centre follow signs to Blackwall Tunnel, turn off Blackwall Lane into Tunnel Avenue then into Drawdock Road
Waters accessed: Rivers Thames and Wey, Grand Union and Oxford canals, North Sea

Bugsby's Hole Causeway, River Way, Greenwich, London

Suits: small craft
Availability: tidal site: launch near HW
Restrictions: access may be congested
Facilities: none
Licence: none
Charge: none
Directions: from Greenwich centre follow signs to Blackwall Tunnel, follow Blackwall Lane, turning off to causeway under A102: site is at end of River Way
Waters accessed: Rivers Thames and Wey, Grand Union and Oxford canals, North Sea

Barge House Road, North Woolwich, London

Type: concrete slipway
Suits: small craft
Availability: tidal site
Restrictions: access may be congested: muddy at LW
Facilities: none
Licence: none
Charge: none
Directions: from A13 at Beckton turn south onto A117 East Ham Manor Way; follow road towards Woolwich Ferry turning left into Barge House Rd
Waters accessed: Rivers Thames and Wey, Grand Union and Oxford canals, North Sea

Bell Water Gate, Woolwich, London

Type: steep concrete slipway
Suits: small craft
Availability: tidal site: launch near HW
Restrictions: steep ramp

Facilities:	parking is difficult
Licence:	none
Charge:	none
Directions:	access is from Woolwich High Street; site is upriver of power station
Waters accessed:	Rivers Thames and Wey, Grand Union and Oxford canals, North Sea

Lower Section (Dagenham – Sea Reach) 01474 562212

Gravesham Marina, Gravesend Promenade, Gravesend, Kent

Tel: 01474 352392

Type:	shallow concrete slipway with winch & crane up to 9 tons
Suits:	all craft except pwc and windsurfers
Availability:	at all states of tide: lock into river opens from 1 hour before to HW
Restrictions:	3 knot speed limit in marina: locked barrier, key from lock-keeper
Facilities:	diesel on site, petrol nearby, parking for car and trailer, toilets, outboard repairs and secure compound on site; chandlery nearby,
Licence:	none
Charge:	approx. £6.50; tide fee (approx. £6) charged for lock opening before 0700 and after 2100 due to tide times
Directions:	from London take A2 following signs to Rochester: at Gravesend east turn off along Valley Drive, turning right into Old Rd East: at roundabout turn left along Rochester Rd to next roundabout then right into Ordnance Road; site is at bottom of road
Waters accessed:	Rivers Thames and Wey, Grand Union and Oxford canals, North Sea

Upper Trent - Waterways Manager, British Waterways, Sawley Marina, Sawley, Nottinghamshire NG10 3AE Tel:0115 973 4278

Lower Trent - Waterways Manager, British Waterways, The Kiln, Mather Lane, Newark, Nottinghamshire NG24 4TT Tel: 01636 704481

The river runs for almost 100 miles from the Midlands to the Humber Estuary, giving access to the Sheffield and South Yorkshire Navigation, the Chesterfield Canal, the Fossdyke and Witham Navigation, the Erewash Canal, the River Soar Navigation and the Trent and Mersey Canal. Below Cromwell Lock the river is tidal. There is a speed limit of 8 mph downstream of Long Eaton and 6 mph upstream. Water-skiing is allowed in some areas.

Shardlow Marina, London Road, Shardlow, Derby
Tel: 01332 792832

Type: steep concrete slipway
Suits: all craft except PWC and windsurfers
Availability: 0900 - 1630 daily by prior arrangement
Restrictions: none
Facilities: diesel, parking for car and trailer(c), sewage and refuse disposal, water, gas, pump-out, toilets and showers, chandlery, restaurant
Licence: BW licence
Charge: approx. £9.50
Directions: leave M1 at junction 24 taking A6 towards Derby
Waters accessed: River Trent and waterways mentioned in paragraph above

Sawley Marina, Sawley, Long Eaton, Nottingham, Notts
Tel: 0115 973 4278

Type: shallow concrete slipway
Suits: all craft except PWC and windsurfers
Availability: 0930 - 1730 daily
Restrictions: pwc prohibited
Facilities: fuel, parking for car and trailer, sewage and refuse disposal, water, gas, pump-out, toilets and showers, overnight moorings, chandlery, boatyard with crane, restaurant
Licence: BW licence
Charge: approx. £7
Directions: leave M1 at junction 24 taking A6 towards Derby then turn right to Long Eaton on B6540
Waters accessed: River Trent and waterways mentioned in paragraph above

Beeston Marina, Riverside Road, Beeston, Rylands, Nottingham
Tel: 0115 922 3168

Type: steep concrete slipway
Suits: all craft except PWC and windsurfers
Availability: 0830 - 1800 daily by prior arrangement
Restrictions: pwc and windsurfers prohibited

Facilities:	fuel, parking for car and trailer, water, gas, toilets, overnight moorings, chandlery, boatyard with crane, bar, coffee shop
Licence:	BW licence
Charge:	approx. £10
Directions:	Follow signs from Beeston town centre to Beeston Railway Station, straight on to canalside and follow signs to the marina
Waters accessed:	River Trent and waterways in paragraph above

Nottingham Castle Marina, Marina Road, Castle Marina Park, Nottingham

Tel: 0115 941 2672

Type:	shallow concrete slipway
Suits:	craft up to approx. 30'/9.1m LOA
Availability:	during working hours
Restrictions:	none
Facilities:	diesel, petrol nearby, parking for car not trailer, sewage and refuse disposal, water, gas, pump-out, toilets and showers, overnight moorings, chandlery, launderette
Licence:	BW licence
Charge:	approx. £8
Directions:	leave M1 at junction 25 taking A52 to city
Waters accessed:	Nottingham Canal, River Trent and waterways in paragraph above

Russell Hunt Marine Centre, The Wharf, Trent Lane, East Bridgford, Nottingham

Tel: 01949 20250

Type:	shallow concrete slipway
Suits:	small craft
Availability:	0900 - 1800 by prior arrangement
Restrictions:	pwc prohibited
Facilities:	parking for car and trailer, toilets, water, diving supplies, chandlery; engine repairs nearby
Licence:	BW licence
Charge:	approx. £7
Directions:	from Nottingham city centre take A6011 through West Bridgford, then A52; at Bingham take A46 then left at roundabout onto A6097; site is ¼ downstream of Gunthorpe Bridge
Waters accessed:	River Trent and waterways mentioned in paragraph above

Ferry Boat Inn, Stoke Bardolph, Nottingham, Notts

Type:	small concrete slipway
Suits:	small craft
Availability:	during daylight hours
Restrictions:	none
Facilities:	fuel, parking for car(c), toilets, telephone, pub adjacent
Licence:	BW licence
Charge:	yes - on application

Directions:	take A612 north east from Nottingham and turn off following signs to the village; site is adjacent to pub
Waters accessed:	River Trent and waterways mentioned in paragraph above

Star and Garter Public House, Hazelford Ferry, Bleasby, Nottingham, Notts

Type:	small concrete slipway
Suits:	small craft
Availability:	during daylight hours
Facilities:	fuel (3 miles), parking for car and trailer(c), toilets, telephone, pub
Licence:	BW licence
Charge:	none
Directions:	take the A612 north-east from Nottingham to Thurgarton: turn right at the Coach and Horses and follow signs to Bleasby
Waters accessed:	River Trent and waterways mentioned in paragraph above

Farndon Marina, North End, Farndon, Newark, Notts

Tel: 01636 705483

Type:	concrete slipway
Suits:	all craft
Availability:	launch during working hours
Restrictions:	none
Facilities:	diesel on site, petrol nearby, parking for car and trailer(c), sewage and refuse disposal, pump-out, water, gas, toilets and showers, telephone, overnight moorings, limited chandlery, boatyard with crane and boat hoist, engine repairs, launderette, restaurant
Licence:	BW licence
Charge:	approx. £12
Directions:	follow A46 south from Newark turning into Farndon main street then right into Marsh Lane, left into Nursery Avenue and right to marina
Waters accessed:	River Trent and waterways mentioned in paragraph above

TRENT AND MERSEY CANAL

BW (Midlands and North West Region)

Trentham to Derwentmouth
Waterway Manager, British Waterways, Fradley Junction, Fradley, Alrewas, Burton-on-Trent, Staffordshire DE13 7DN Tel: 01283 790236

Preston Brook to Trentham
Waterway Manager, British Waterways, Red Bull Yard, Congleton Road South, Church Lawton, Stoke on Trent ST7 3AP Tel: 01782 785703

The canal runs for 93 miles from Derwentmouth to Preston Brook and has junctions with a number of other canals. It was an extremely successful waterway, carrying china clay and flint for the potteries and taking away finished goods. There is a speed limit of 4 mph.

Sawley Marina, Sawley, Long Eaton, Nottingham, Notts

Tel: 0115 973 4278

For details see page 90 under River Trent

Dobsons Boatyard. The Wharf, Shardlow, Derby

Tel: 01332 792271 (Canal Craft (Brokerage) Ltd)

Type:	shallow concrete slipway
Suits:	small powered craft, canoes and rowing dingies
Availability:	0900 - 1800 daily by prior arrangement
Restrictions:	none
Facilities:	diesel, petrol nearby, parking for car and trailer(c), sewage and refuse disposal, water, gas, pump-out, toilets, overnight moorings, chandlery nearby, boatyard
Licence:	BW licence
Charge:	approx. £10
Directions:	leave M1 at junction 24 taking the A50 towards Derby then old A6 to Shardlow village; site is down road to right
Waters accessed:	River Trent, Erewash Canal, River Soar Navigation, Coventry Canal, Staffs and Worcs Canal, Caldon Canal, Macclesfield Canal

Midland Canal Centre, Stenson Marina, Stenson, Derbyshire

Tel: 01283 701933

Type:	concrete slipway
Suits:	all craft
Availability:	during working hours by prior arrangement only
Restrictions:	none
Facilities:	diesel, petrol nearby, parking for car and trailer(c), sewage disposal, water, gas, pump-out, toilets, overnight moorings, chandlery and boatyard
Licence:	BW licence
Charge:	yes - on application

Directions:	follow the A38 south from Derby taking the A5132 east to Twyford, then follow minor roads
Waters accessed:	River Trent, Erewash Canal, River Soar Navigation, Coventry Canal, Staffs and Worcs Canal, Caldon Canal, Macclesfield Canal

Shobnall Marina, Shobnall Road, Burton-on-Trent, Derbyshire

Tel: 01283 542718 (Jannel Cruisers Ltd)

Type:	shallow concrete slipway
Suits:	all craft
Availability:	during working hours by prior arrangement only
Restrictions:	locked barrier out of working hours
Facilities:	diesel, petrol nearby, parking for car and trailer(c), sewage and refuse disposal, water, gas, pump-out, toilets, chandlery, overnight moorings, boatyard
Licence:	BW licence
Charge:	approx. £5
Directions:	leave the A38 at South Burton turn off signposted A5121 Burton: turn left onto B5234 for two miles and turn left at traffic island: the site is then 200m along Shobnall Road on the left hand side
Waters accessed:	River Trent, Erewash Canal, River Soar Navigation, Coventry Canal, Staffs and Worcs Canal, Caldon Canal, Macclesfield Canal

The Stone Boatbuilding Co Ltd, Newcastle Road, Stone, Staffs

Tel: 01785 812688

Type:	concrete slipway
Suits:	narrow boats and canal cruisers
Availability:	0900 - 1730 mon - fri and 1000 - 1600 sun (Apr - Nov) by prior arrangement
Restrictions:	locked gate out of working hours; no launching sat
Facilities:	diesel, petrol nearby, parking for car and trailer(c) by arrangement only, sewage and refuse disposal, water, gas, pump-out (not sun), toilets, chandlery, boatyard, engine repairs
Licence:	BW licence
Charge:	approx. £5
Directions:	follow the A34 south turning off into Stone and onto B5027
Waters accessed:	River Trent, Erewash Canal, River Soar Navigation, Coventry Canal, Staffs and Worcs Canal, Caldon Canal, Macclesfield Canal

Dolphin Boats, Old Whieldon Road, Stoke-on-Trent, Staffs

Tel: 01782 849390

Type:	medium concrete slipway
Suits:	all craft up to 30'/9.1m LOA
Availability:	during daylight hours by prior arrangement
Restrictions:	none

Facilities: fuel nearby, parking for car and trailer(c), water, gas, overnight moorings, chandlery, boatyard, engine repairs
Licence: BW licence
Charge: approx, £6
Directions: from M6 junction 15 take A500; at first roundabout turn completely round and take first left sliproad: site is by bridge 112
Waters accessed: River Trent, Erewash Canal, River Soar Navigation, Coventry Canal, Staffs and Worcs Canal, Caldon Canal, Macclesfield Canal

Longport Wharf, Longport, Stoke-on-Trent, Staffs

Tel: 01782 813831 (Stoke-on-Trent Boatbuilding)

Type: shallow concrete slipway
Suits: small powered craft, canoes, sailing and rowing dinghies
Availability: 0900 - 1700 daily
Restrictions: none
Facilities: diesel, parking for car and trailer(c), sewage and refuse disposal, water, gas, pump-out, toilets, overnight moorings, boatyard, engine repairs
Licence: BW licence
Charge: approx. £10
Directions: leave the M6 at junction 15/16 taking the A500 to Stone, then A527 for Tunstall; site is 400m on right
Waters accessed: River Trent, Erewash Canal, River Soar Navigation, Coventry Canal, Staffs and Worcs Canal, Caldon Canal, Macclesfield Canal

Orchard Marina, School Road, Rudheath, Northwich Cheshire

Tel: 01606 42082

Type: concrete slipway
Suits: all craft up to 25'/7.6m LOA
Availability: by prior arrangement only
Restrictions: none
Facilities: diesel, parking for car and trailer(c), sewage and refuse disposal, water, gas, pump-out, toilets and showers, overnight moorings, boatyard, launderette
Licence: BW licence
Charge: approx. £10
Directions: at junction for Gadbrooke Road on A556 by Roberts Bakery follow signs to Gadbrooke Business Centre: site is on opposite side of canal
Waters accessed: River Trent, Erewash Canal, River Soar Navigation, Coventry Canal, Staffs and Worcs Canal, Caldon Canal, Macclesfield Canal

Anderton Marina. Uplands Road, Anderton, Northwich, Cheshire

Tel: 01606 79642 (Alvechurch Boat Centres Ltd)

Type:	small slipway
Suits:	small powered craft, canoes and rowing dinghies
Availability:	by prior arrangement only
Restrictions:	not suitable for large boats or vehicles
Facilities:	diesel, parking for car and trailer(c), sewage and refuse disposal, water, gas, pump-out, toilets, overnight moorings, boat hire
Licence:	BW licence
Charge:	approx. £10
Directions:	from the M6 take M56 west, exiting at junction 10; at roundabout take A559 signposted Northwich and after 4½ miles turn right to Comberbach. Continue through village and past Marbury Country Park to Anderton; site is just after village sign on left
Waters accessed:	River Trent, Erewash Canal, River Soar Navigation, Coventry Canal, Staffs and Worcs Canal, Caldon Canal, Macclesfield Canal

RIVER TYNE

Port of Tyne Authority
Tel: 0191 2325541

This is a busy commercial river: all boats are subject to a minimum conservancy charge by the Port of Tyne Authority. There is a speed limit of 6 mph on the river and all waterborne activities are subject to the Authority's bylaws.

Hebburn Riverside Park, Prince Consort Road, Hebburn, Tyne and Wear

Tel: 0191 2640014 (Newburn Leisure Centre)

Type:	very steep concrete slipway
Suits:	small powered craft
Availability:	approx. 4 hours either side of HW: site is used by Hebburn Marina Boat Club
Restrictions:	no water-skiing
Facilities:	fuel and parking for car and trailer nearby
Licence:	Port of Tyne Authority
Charge:	approx. £6.50
Directions:	from A69 take the A6085 for Throckley / Newburn turning off into Grange Road and following signs to 'Hebburn Riverside Park'
Waters accessed:	River Tyne and North Sea

Friar's Goose Water Sports Club, Riverside Park, Green Lane, Gateshead

Tel: 0191 4692545 or 0191 4692952 (eves)

Type:	concrete slipway
Suits:	all trailable craft
Availability:	launching for 2 - 3 hours either side HW
Restrictions:	none
Facilities:	fuel from local garage, parking for car and trailer, toilets and showers nearby, overnight moorings
Licence:	Port of Tyne Authority

Charge: approx. £5
Directions: follow A6127 from the A1(M) into Gateshead: site is on south bank and access is via Green Lane
Waters accessed: River Tyne and North Sea

Derwenthaugh Marina, Blaydon, Gateshead, Tyne and Wear

Tel: 0191 4140065 (Powerhouse Marine)

Type: two medium concrete ramps
Suits: craft up to 35'/10.7m LOA
Availability: launching for approximately 4 hours either side HW
Restrictions: all craft launching must have third party insurance; fast water zone downstream
Facilities: fuel nearby, parking for car and trailer, toilets, showers, changing rooms, telephone, chandlers, engine repairs, moorings
Licence: Port of Tyne Authority
Charge: approx. £7
Directions: from A1 follow signs to Blaydon (A695) and look for blue building with 'ARCO': follow narrow road past this building to marina
Waters accessed: River Tyne and North Sea

St Peters Marina, St Peters Basin, Newcastle, Tyne and Wear

Tel: 0191 265 4472

Type: 3 ton static crane
Suits: all craft
Availability: launching for approximately 4 hours either side HW 0900 - 1700 by prior arrangement
Restrictions: all craft launching must have third party insurance; fast water zone downstream
Facilities: fuel, parking for car and trailer, water, pump-out, toilets, showers, telephone, chandlers, engine repairs, moorings
Licence: Port of Tyne Authority
Charge: approx. £20
Directions: from A1 follow A692 or A184 and cross river; site is on Quayside downstream of bridge
Waters accessed: River Tyne and North Sea

British Waterways, Rosebank House, Main Street, Camelon, Falkirk FK1 4DS
Tel: 01324 671217 Fax: 01324 671225

Built in the 19th century to transport coal to Edinburgh and originally connected to the Forth and Clyde Canal at Falkirk by a flight of 11 locks.The canal is now being restored, the flight of locks being replaced by the 'Falkirk Wheel', and is due to re-open to complete navigation early in 2002. The canal is 31½ miles long and has a speed limit of 3 mph.

Manse Road Basin, Manse Road, Linlithgow, Lothian

Type: stone and concrete slipway
Suits: craft up to 13'/4m LOA and 7'/2.1m wide
Availability: during daylight hours
Restrictions: site is regularly used by local canal society
Facilities: parking for car and trailer by arrangement, toilets; fuel nearby
Licence: BW licence
Charge: none
Directions: follow the B9080 west from Edinburgh; site is near railway station
Waters accessed: Union and Forth & Clyde canals

East Church Street, Broxburn, Nr. Linlithgow, Lothian

Type: concrete
Suits: craft up to 25'/7.6m LOA
Availability: during daylight hours
Restrictions: key to gate from BW
Facilities: parking for cars; fuel, toilets and telephone nearby
Licence: BW licence
Charge: none
Directions: follow the A8, A89/899 west from Edinburgh: access is off East Main Road and the site is near Broxburn Sports Centre
Waters accessed: Union and Forth & Clyde canals

Harrison Park, Edinburgh

Type: small wooden ramp
Suits: craft up to 13'/4m LOA
Availability: during daylight hours
Restrictions: this area is regularly used by rowers
Facilities: fuel, parking for cars, toilets and telephone nearby
Licence: BW licence
Charge: none
Directions: turn off A70 Slateford Road into Harrison Road then into Harrison Gardens: site is on corner of Ashley Drive and Ogilvy Terrace
Waters accessed: Union and Forth & Clyde canals

Port of Sunderland
Tel: 0191-553 2100

This is a busy commercial river with a speed limit of 6 knots. Access to the sea from the upper reaches is limited to 3 hours either side HW by a barrier.

Claxhaugh, Sunderland, Tyne and Wear

Type:	shallow concrete slipway
Suits:	craft up to 20'/6.1m LOA
Availability:	approx. 3 hours either side HW
Restrictions:	tidal site four miles from river mouth; water-skiing permitted in designated area; pwc and windsurfers prohibited
Facilities:	parking for car and trailer
Licence:	none
Charge:	approx. £6+vat
Directions:	from A19 turn onto A183 at sign 'Sunderland South': turn left at first roundabout, left at next roundabout and ask for directions when river is reached: site is 4 miles from river mouth
Waters accessed:	River Wear and North Sea

Sunderland Marina, Roker, Sunderland, Tyne & Wear
Tel: 0191 5144721 (Marina Manager)

Type:	medium concrete slipway into river
Suits:	all craft
Availability:	all states of tide by prior arrangement
Restrictions:	6 knot speed limit in harbour and river: water-skiing permitted only in designated area; locked barrier to slipway
Facilities:	diesel on site, petrol nearby, parking for car and trailer, toilets and showers nearby; overnight berths in marina with 24 hour access
Dues:	none
Charge:	approx £80 p.a.
Directions:	from A1 take A690 and A19 north; turn right onto A1231 east to Roker following signs to seafront and 'National Glass Centre': site gives access to River Wear 10 mins from the open sea
Waters accessed:	River Wear and North Sea

RIVER WEY AND GODALMING NAVIGATION (National Trust)

Dapdune Wharf, Wharf Road, Guildford GU1 4RR
Tel: 01483 561389 Fax: 01483 531667

The river joins the Thames below Shepperton Lock and is owned by the National Trust. It is navigable for nearly 20 miles to Godalming and gives access to the Basingstoke Canal at Woodham Junction. There is a speed limit of 4 knots and engine size is restricted to 1 HP per foot length up to a max size of 20 HP.

Pyrford Marina, Lock Lane, Pyrford, Woking, Surrey

Tel: 01932 340739

Type:	shallow concrete slipway
Suits:	small powered craft (not ribs), canoes and rowing dinghies
Availability:	daily 0900 - 1300 and 1400 - 1700: closed tues
Restrictions:	do not approach via Ripley Road: there is a narrow bridge: craft must have 3rd party insurance and current Boat Safety Certificate
Facilities:	diesel, petrol nearby, parking for car and trailer(c), sewage and refuse disposal, water, gas, pump-out, toilets and showers, boatyard
Licence:	National Trust
Charge:	approx. £10
Directions:	from M25 junction 10 follow A3 to Cobham roundabout, taking A245 to West Byfleet and turning off down Pyrford Road then into Lock Lane: site is by gate into marina
Waters accessed:	River Wey, River Thames, Basingstoke Canal (separate licence required)

Stoke Lock, Guildford, Surrey

Tel: 01483 504939 or 07703 326076

Type:	concrete slipway
Suits:	craft up to 25'/7.6m LOA with appropriate engine size
Availability:	daylight hours by prior arrangement only
Restrictions:	locked barrier
Facilities:	parking for car and trailer, telephone
Licence:	National Trust
Charge:	approx. £6 inc. parking
Directions:	turn off the A320 Woking road at the Slyfield Industrial Estate into Moorfield Road. Turn right into the trackway immediately before next small roundabout, passing Acorn Engineering on left: site is adjacent Thames Water
Waters accessed:	River Wey, River Thames, Basingstoke Canal (separate licence required)

Dapdune Wharf, Guildford, Surrey

Tel: 01483 561389 (0900 - 1700 mon - thurs, 0900 - 1600 fri)

Type:	steep concrete slipway
Suits:	craft up to 25'/7.6m LOA with appropriate engine size
Availability:	daylight hours by prior arrangement only

Restrictions:	locked gate
Facilities:	parking for car and trailer, telephone
Licence:	National Trust
Charge:	approx. £6 inc. parking
Directions:	turn off A322 (Woodbridge Road) into Wharf Road: Dapdune Wharf is immediately behind cricket ground
Waters accessed:	River Wey, River Thames, Basingstoke Canal (separate licence required)

RIVER WITHAM (WITHAM AND FOSSDYKE NAVIGATION)
BW (North East Region)

Waterways Manager, British Waterways, The Kiln, Mather Lane, Newark, Nottinghamshire NG24 4TT Tel: 01636 704481

The Fossdyke Navigation is the oldest artificially constructed waterway in the country and was designed to connect the River Witham to the Trent and Humber. There is a speed limit of 3 mph.

Brayford Wharf East, Brayford Pool, Lincoln, Lincs
Tel: 01522 521452 (Brayford Trust)

Type:	steep concrete slipway
Suits:	craft up to 18'/5.4m LOA
Availability:	during daylight hours
Restrictions:	difficult access to slipway
Facilities:	fuel, parking for cars and trailer (c), toilets, chandlery and boatyard all nearby
Licence:	BW licence
Charge:	none
Directions:	from City centre, take Wigford Way to Brayford Pool
Waters accessed:	Witham Navigable Drains, River Trent, Humber Estuary

James Kendall and Co. Lincoln Marina, Brayford Pool, Lincoln, Lincs
Tel: 01522 526896

Type:	concrete slipway
Suits:	all craft
Availability:	0900 - 1700 daily
Restrictions:	none
Facilities:	diesel, parking for car and trailer(c), refuse disposal, water, gas, telephone, toilets, showers, overnight moorings, chandlery and boatyard
Licence:	BW licence
Charge:	yes - on application
Directions:	from City centre, take Wigford Way to Brayford Pool
Waters accessed:	Witham Navigable Drains, River Trent, Humber Estuary

Belle Isle Marina, Dogdyke Road, Coningsby, Lincs

Tel: 01526 342124

Type:	steep concrete slipway
Suits:	craft up to 22'/6.7m LOA
Availability:	during working hours
Restrictions:	none
Facilities:	parking for car and trailer, water, toilets and showers, overnight moorings, boatyard
Licence:	BW licence
Charge:	approx. £6
Directions:	from A153 north of Sleaford take Dogdyke Road for 2 miles until sharp left hand bend: site immediately on right
Waters accessed:	Witham Navigable Drains, River Trent, Humber Estuary

WORCESTER AND BIRMINGHAM CANAL BW (Midland Region)

Waterway Manager, British Waterways, Brome Hall Lane, Lapworth, Solihull, West Midlands, B94 5RB Tel: 01564 784634

Now part of the popular cruising circuit, the canal runs for 30 miles from Diglis in Worcester, where it connects with the River Severn to King's Norton where the Stratford-on-Avon Canal enters and ends in Birmingham.The speed limit is 4 mph.

Alvechurch Boat Centre, Scarfield Wharf, Alvechurch, Birmingham

Tel: 0121 445 1133

Type:	narrow concrete slipway or crane
Suits:	all powered craft, canoes and rowing dinghies
Availability:	by prior arrangement only: no casual launching
Restrictions:	locked barrier out of hours
Facilities:	diesel, parking for car and trailer(c), sewage and refuse disposal, water, gas, pump-out, toilets, chandlery
Licence:	BW licence
Charge:	yes - on application
Directions:	from M42 junction 2 take A441 towards Birmingham, at next roundabout turn left and follow signs to Alvechurch. After traffic lights in village centre turn right into Bear Hill; site is on left after railway and canal bridges
Waters accessed:	Worcester Birmingham, Stratford-on-Avon and Birmingham canals, River Severn

Index